McDougal Littell
Geometry
Concepts and Skills

Larson   Boswell   Stiff

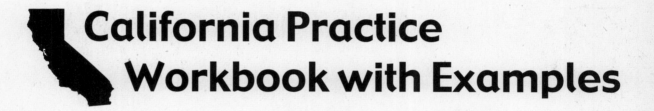

California Practice
Workbook with Examples

The Practice Workbook provides additional practice with
worked-out examples for every lesson. The workbook
covers essential skills and vocabulary. Space is provided
for students to show their work. Two CAHSEE Practice
Tests are also included.

McDougal Littell
A HOUGHTON MIFFLIN COMPANY
Evanston, Illinois • Boston • Dallas

ISBN 0-618-31829-1

Printed in the United States of America.

1 2 3 4 5 6 7 8 9 — MDO — 06 05 04 03 02

Contents

Note to the Teacher

The following workbook contains practice worksheets for all lessons in McDougal Littell's *Geometry Concepts and Skills*. The worksheets are correlated to the California Geometry Content Standards.

The two practice California High School Exit Exams in the back of this booklet are to be used at your discretion. Many teachers may wish to use one at the beginning of the year as a diagnostic test and the second before the test as a final practice before the actual exam. Others may want to break up the exam items by the standards covered and teach them at regular intervals throughout the school year. The answer keys provide correlations to the California objectives covered on the exam.

To use the pages in this book, you will need to make photocopies for all students in your classes.

NAME_____ DATE _____

Reteaching with Practice

For use with pages 3–7

CALIFORNIA
Geometry Content Standards
1.0

GOAL Find patterns and use them to make predictions.

EXAMPLE 1 *Describe a Visual Pattern*

Describe a pattern in the figures.

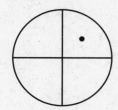
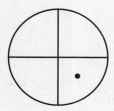

SOLUTION

Each figure looks like the previous one rotated 90°.

Exercises for Example 1

Describe a pattern in the figures.

1.

2.

EXAMPLE 2 *Describe a Number Pattern*

Describe a pattern in the numbers.

a. 22, 28, 34, 40, . . .   **b.** −4, −8, −16, −32, . . .

SOLUTION

a. Each number after the first is 6 more than the previous number.

b. Each number after the first is 2 times the previous number.

NAME_____ DATE _____

Reteaching with Practice

For use with pages 3–7

Exercises for Example 2

Describe a pattern in the numbers.

3. $-6, -7, -8, -9, \ldots$ **4.** $10, 30, 90, 270, \ldots$

EXAMPLE 3 *Make a Prediction*

Sketch the next figure you expect in the pattern.

SOLUTION

The shaded half of the square moves in the counter-clockwise direction each time. The fourth figure will have the lower half of the square shaded.

Exercises for Example 3

Sketch the next figure you expect in the pattern.

5.   **6.**

Geometry, Concepts and Skills
Practice Workbook with Examples

Reteaching with Practice

For use with pages 3–7

EXAMPLE 4 *Make a Prediction*

Write the next two numbers you expect in the pattern.

   $-10, -6, -2, 2, \ldots$

SOLUTION

Each number after the first is 4 more than the previous number. The next two numbers will be 6 and 10.

$-10, -6, -2, 2, 6, 10$

Exercises for Example 4

Write the next two numbers you expect in the pattern.

7. 3, 6, 12, 24, . . .

8. 4, 1, −2, −5, . . .

NAME_____ DATE _____

Reteaching with Practice

For use with pages 8–13

CALIFORNIA
Geometry Content Standards
1.0

GOAL **Use inductive reasoning to make conjectures.**

VOCABULARY

A **conjecture** is an unproven statement that is based on a pattern or observation.

Inductive reasoning is a process that involves looking for patterns and making conjectures.

A **counterexample** is an example that shows a conjecture is false.

EXAMPLE 1 *Make a Conjecture*

Complete the conjecture.

Conjecture: The square of an even number is ___?___.

SOLUTION

Begin by writing several examples.

$2^2 = 4$	$4^2 = 16$	$6^2 = 36$
$8^2 = 64$	$10^2 = 100$	$12^2 = 144$

Each result is even. You can make the following conjecture.

Conjecture: The square of an even number is *even*.

Exercise for Example 1

Complete the conjecture based on the pattern in the examples.

1. *Conjecture:* The sum of any two even numbers and any one odd number is ___?___.

   EXAMPLES

$2 + 4 + 5 = 11$	$4 + 18 + 1 = 13$	$6 + 8 + 7 = 21$
$10 + 12 + 11 = 33$	$2 + 2 + 27 = 31$	$10 + 20 + 21 = 51$

Geometry, Concepts and Skills
Practice Workbook with Examples

NAME _____ DATE _____

Reteaching with Practice

For use with pages 8–13

EXAMPLE 2 *Make a Conjecture*

Complete the conjecture.

Conjecture: The sum of the first n even positive integers is __?__ .

SOLUTION

Begin by writing several examples.

When $n = 1$ When $n = 2$
$2 = 1 \times 2$ $2 + 4 = 6 = 2 \times 3$

When $n = 3$ When $n = 4$
$2 + 4 + 6 = 12 = 3 \times 4$ $2 + 4 + 6 + 8 = 20 = 4 \times 5$

Each time, the sum of the numbers can be written as the product of n and $n + 1$.

Conjecture: The sum of the first n even positive integers is equal to $n(n + 1)$.

Exercise for Example 2

Complete the conjecture based on the pattern in the examples.

2. *Conjecture:* The product of 5 and any even number is divisible by __?__ .

     EXAMPLES

     $5 \times 2 = 10 = 10 \times 1$ $5 \times 4 = 20 = 10 \times 2$ $5 \times 6 = 30 = 10 \times 3$

     $5 \times 8 = 40 = 10 \times 4$ $5 \times 14 = 70 = 10 \times 7$ $5 \times 100 = 500 = 10 \times 50$

EXAMPLE 3 *Find a Counterexample*

Show the conjecture is false by finding a counterexample.

Conjecture: The difference of two even numbers is positive.

SOLUTION

Here is a counterexample. Let the two even numbers be 6 and 8. The difference $6 - 8$ is -2, which is not positive. The conjecture is false.

Geometry, Concepts and Skills
Practice Workbook with Examples

Reteaching with Practice

For use with pages 8–13

Exercises for Example 3

Show the conjecture is false by finding a counterexample.

3. The product of −1 and any number is negative.

4. Any number that is divisible by 5 is divisible by 10.

EXAMPLE 3 *Find a Counterexample*

Show the conjecture is false by finding a counterexample.

Conjecture: If a triangle is drawn inside of a circle with two corners of the triangle touching the circle, then the third corner of the triangle will also touch the circle.

SOLUTION

A counterexample is shown at the right. In the drawing, the triangle is inside the circle, with two corners touching the circle. The third corner of the triangle is *not* touching the circle. The conjecture is false.

Exercise for Example 4

Show the conjecture is false by finding a counterexample.

5. If two circles touch each other, then one circle is inside the other.

Geometry, Concepts and Skills
Practice Workbook with Examples

NAME _____ DATE _____

Reteaching with Practice

For use with pages 14–20

CALIFORNIA
Geometry Content Standards
1.0

GOAL   **Use postulates and undefined terms.**

VOCABULARY

Undefined terms are terms that cannot be mathematically defined using other known words.

A **point** has no dimension, a **line** has one dimension, and a **plane** has two dimensions.

A **postulate** is a statement that is accepted without further justification.

Collinear points are points that lie on the same line.

Coplanar points are points that lie on the same plane.

Coplanar lines are lines that lie on the same plane.

The **segment** $\overline{AB}$ consists of the **endpoints** A and B, and all points on $\overleftrightarrow{AB}$ that are between A and B.

The **ray** $\overrightarrow{AB}$ consists of the endpoint A and all points on $\overleftrightarrow{AB}$ that lie on the same side of A as B.

Postulate 1   Two Points Determine a Line

    Through any two points there is exactly one line.

Postulate 2   Three Points Determine a Plane

    Through any three points not on a line there is exactly one plane.

EXAMPLE 1   *Name Points, Lines, and Planes*

Use the diagram at the right.

a. Name four points.

b. Name two lines.

c. Name two planes.

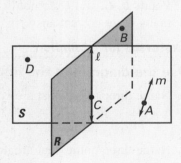

SOLUTION

a. A, B, C, and D are points.

b. Line ℓ and line m

c. R and S are planes.

NAME _____ DATE _____

Reteaching with Practice

For use with pages 14–20

Exercises for Example 1

Use the figure at the right.

1. Name five points.

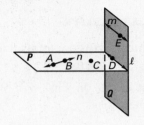

2. Name three lines.

3. Name two planes.

EXAMPLE 2 *Name Collinear and Coplanar Points*

Use the diagram at the right.

a. Name three points that are collinear.

b. Name four points that are coplanar.

c. Name three points that are not collinear.

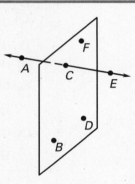

SOLUTION

a. Points *A*, *C*, and *E* lie on the same line. So, they are collinear.

b. Points *B*, *C*, *D*, and *F* lie on the same plane. So, the are coplanar.

c. Points *B*, *C*, and *D* do not lie on the same line, so they are not collinear. There are many other correct answers.

Exercises for Example 2

Use the diagram at the right.

4. Name three points that are collinear.

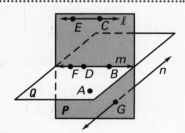

5. Name three points that are not collinear.

6. Name four points that are coplanar.

7. Name four points that are not coplanar.

8. Name two lines that are coplanar.

Geometry, Concepts and Skills
Practice Workbook with Examples

LESSON
1.3
CONTINUED

Reteaching with Practice

For use with pages 14–16

EXAMPLE 3 *Draw Lines, Segments, and Rays*

Draw four points as shown.
Then draw $\overrightarrow{AB}$, $\overleftrightarrow{CD}$, and $\overline{AC}$.

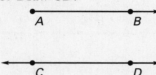

SOLUTION

1. Draw A, B, C, and D.

2. Draw $\overrightarrow{AB}$.

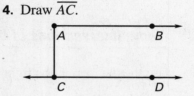

3. Draw $\overleftrightarrow{CD}$.

4. Draw $\overline{AC}$.

Exercise for Example 3

9. Draw four points A, B, C, and D, no three of which are collinear. Sketch $\overleftrightarrow{AB}$, $\overleftrightarrow{CD}$, $\overline{AC}$, $\overrightarrow{AD}$, and $\overrightarrow{CB}$.

Geometry, Concepts and Skills
Practice Workbook with Examples

NAME _____ DATE _____

Reteaching with Practice

For use with pages 21–27

CALIFORNIA
Geometry Content Standards
16.0

GOAL Sketch simple figures and their intersections.

VOCABULARY

In geometry, figures **intersect** if they have any points in common.

The **intersection** of two or more figures is the point or points that the figures have in common.

Postulate 3   Intersection of Two Lines

   If two lines intersect, then their intersection is a point.

Postulate 4   Intersection of Two Planes

   If two planes intersect, then their intersection is a line.

EXAMPLE 1 *Name Intersections of Lines*

Use the diagram at the right.

a. Name the intersection of $\overleftrightarrow{PR}$ and $\overleftrightarrow{SU}$.

b. Name the intersection of $\overleftrightarrow{QT}$ and $\overleftrightarrow{SU}$.

c. Name the intersection of $\overleftrightarrow{QT}$ and $\overleftrightarrow{PR}$.

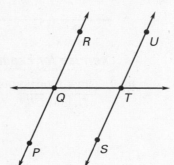

SOLUTION

a. $\overleftrightarrow{PR}$ and $\overleftrightarrow{SU}$ do not appear to intersect.

b. $\overleftrightarrow{QT}$ and $\overleftrightarrow{SU}$ intersect at point T.

c. $\overleftrightarrow{QT}$ and $\overleftrightarrow{PR}$ intersect at point Q.

Exercises for Example 1

Use the diagram at the right.

1. Name the intersection of $\overleftrightarrow{AB}$ and $\overleftrightarrow{BC}$.

2. Name the intersection of $\overleftrightarrow{AB}$ and $\overleftrightarrow{ED}$.

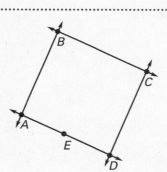

3. Name the intersection of $\overleftrightarrow{AB}$ and $\overleftrightarrow{CD}$.

4. Name the intersection of $\overleftrightarrow{BC}$ and $\overleftrightarrow{CD}$.

NAME _____ DATE _____

Reteaching with Practice

For use with pages 21–27

EXAMPLE 2 *Name Intersections of Planes*

Use the diagram at the right.

a. Name the intersection of planes P and Q.

b. Name the intersection of planes P and R.

c. Name the intersection of planes R and Q.

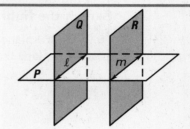

SOLUTION

a. Planes P and Q intersect at line ℓ.

b. Planes P and R intersect at line m.

c. Planes R and Q do not appear to intersect.

Exercises for Example 2

Use the diagram at the right.

5. Name the intersection of planes S and T.

6. Name the intersection of planes T and R.

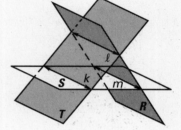

7. Name the intersection of planes R and S.

EXAMPLE 3 *Sketch Intersections of Lines and Planes*

Sketch the figure described.

a. two lines that intersect in a point

b. two lines that lie in a plane

SOLUTION

a. Draw a line. Then draw a line that intersects the first line.

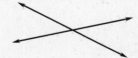

b. Draw the plane. Then draw two lines that are in the plane.

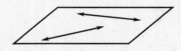

NAME_____ DATE _____

Reteaching with Practice

Exercises for Example 3

Sketch the figure described.

8. Sketch a plane and a line that intersects the plane. Then sketch a line in the plane that intersects the first line.

9. Sketch a plane and a line that intersects the plane. Then sketch another line that intersects the plane and does not intersect the first line.

10. Sketch two planes that intersect in a line. Then sketch a line that intersects each of the planes, but does not intersect the first line.

Geometry, Concepts and Skills
Practice Workbook with Examples

LESSON 1.5

Reteaching with Practice

For use with pages 28–33

CALIFORNIA
Geometry Content Standards
17.0

GOAL Measure segments. Add segment lengths.

VOCABULARY

The real number that corresponds to a point is the **coordinate** of a point.

The **distance** between points A and B, written AB, is the absolute value of the difference of the coordinates of A and B.

AB is also called the **length** of $\overline{AB}$.

When three points lie on a line, one of them is **between** the other two.

Segments that have the same length are called **congruent segments.**

Postulate 5   Segment Addition Postulate

If B is between A and C, then $AC = AB + BC$.

If $AC = AB + BC$, then B is between A and C.

EXAMPLE 1   *Find the Distance Between Two Points*

Measure the total width of the processor chip to the nearest $\frac{1}{8}$ inch. Then measure the width of the dark-colored square inside the rows of circles.

SOLUTION

Use a ruler to measure in inches.

1. Align the zero mark of the ruler with one end of the processor chip.

2. Find the width of the processor chip, AD.
$$AD = \left| 1\frac{7}{8} - 0 \right| = 1\frac{7}{8}$$

3. Find the width of the dark-colored square inside the rows of circles, BC.
$$BC = \left| 1\frac{1}{2} - \frac{3}{8} \right| = 1\frac{1}{8}$$

The total width of the processor is $1\frac{7}{8}$ in.
The width of the dark-colored square is $1\frac{1}{8}$ in.

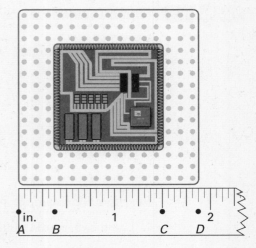

Exercises for Example 1

Use a ruler to measure the length of the segment to the nearest $\frac{1}{8}$ inch.

1. $E \bullet\!\!-\!\!-\!\!-\!\!-\!\!-\!\!-\!\!-\!\!-\!\!-\!\!-\!\!-\!\!-\!\!-\!\!-\!\!\bullet F$ 2. $G \bullet\!\!-\!\!-\!\!-\!\!-\!\!\bullet H$

Reteaching with Practice

EXAMPLE 2 *Find a Distance by Adding*

Use the diagram to find *AC*.

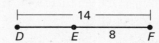

SOLUTION

Because the three points lie on the same line, you can use the Segment Addition Postulate.

$AC = AB + BC$ Segment Addition Postulate

$AC = 10 + 3$ Substitute 10 for *AB* and 3 for *BC*.

$AC = 13$ Add.

Exercise for Example 2

3. Use the diagram to find *JL*.

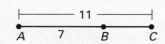

EXAMPLE 3 *Find a Distance by Subtracting*

Use the diagram to find *DE*.

SOLUTION

$DF = DE + EF$ Segment Addition Postulate

$14 = DE + 8$ Substitute 14 for *DF* and 8 for *EF*.

$6 = DE$ Subtract 8 from both sides.

Exercise for Example 3

4. Use the diagram to find *BC*.

NAME_____ DATE_____

Reteaching with Practice

For use with pages 28–33

EXAMPLE 4 *Decide Whether Segments are Congruent*

Are the segments shown in the coordinate plane congruent?

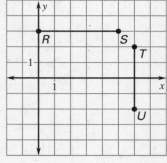

SOLUTION

For a horizontal segment, subtract *x*-coordinates.

$RS = |0 - 5| = |-5| = 5$

For a vertical segment, subtract the *y*-coordinates.

$TU = |2 - (-2)| = |-4| = 4$

$\overline{TU}$ and $\overline{RS}$ have different lengths. So $\overline{TU}$ and $\overline{RS}$ are *not* congruent.

Exercises for Example 4
....

Plot the points in a coordinate plane. Then draw segments $\overline{AB}$ and $\overline{CD}$. Decide if $\overline{AB}$ and $\overline{CD}$ are congruent.

5. $A(4, 2), B(4, -1), C(8, 5), D(11, 5)$ **6.** $A(5, 10), B(-5, 10), C(-2, -2), D(-2, 2)$

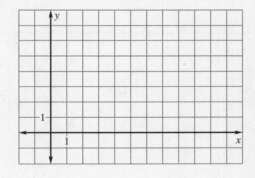 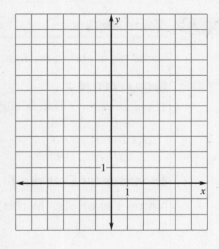

Reteaching with Practice

For use with pages 34–41

CALIFORNIA
Geometry Content Standards
1.0

GOAL Measure and classify angles. Add angle measures.

VOCABULARY

An **angle** consists of two rays that have the same endpoint.

The rays are the **sides** of the angle. The endpoint is the **vertex** of the angle.

The **measure** of an angle is written in units called **degrees** (°).

Two angles are **congruent angles** if they have the same measure.

An **acute angle** has measure between 0° and 90°.

A **right angle** has measure 90°.

An **obtuse angle** has measure between 90° and 180°.

A **straight angle** has measure 180°.

Postulate 6   Angle Addition Postulate

If *P* is in the interior of ∠*RST*, then the measure of ∠*RST* is the sum of the measures of ∠*RSP* and ∠*PST*.

EXAMPLE 1 *Name Angles*

Name the angles in the figure.

SOLUTION

There are three different angles.
∠*ABC* or ∠*CBA*
∠*CBD* or ∠*DBC*
∠*ABD* or ∠*DBA*

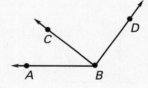

Exercises for Example 1

Name the angles in the figure.

1.

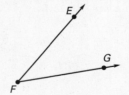

2.

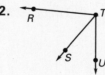

NAME _____ DATE _____

Reteaching with Practice

For use with pages 34–41

EXAMPLE 2 *Measure Angles*

Use a protractor to approximate the measure of ∠DEF.

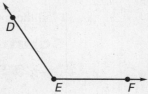

SOLUTION

1. Place the center of the protractor over the vertex point *E*.

2. Align the protractor with one side of the angle.

3. The second side of the angle crosses the protractor at the 123° mark. So, m∠DEF = 123°.

Exercises for Example 2

Use a protractor to approximate the measure of ∠ABC.

3.

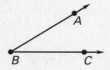

4. ←——•——————•——————•——→
       A   *B*   *C*

EXAMPLE 3 *Classify Angles*

Classify each angle as *acute, right, obtuse,* or *straight.*

a. m∠D = 142°   **b.** m∠E = 180°   **c.** m∠F = 7°

SOLUTION

a. ∠D is *obtuse* because its measure is between 90° and 180°.

b. ∠E is *straight* because its measure is 180°.

c. ∠F is *acute* because its measure is between 0° and 90°.

Exercises for Example 3

Classify the angle as *acute, right, obtuse,* or *straight.*

5. m∠A = 90°   **6.** m∠B = 82°   **7.** m∠C = 155°

NAME_____ DATE _____

Reteaching with Practice

For use with pages 35–41

EXAMPLE 4 *Subtract Angle Measures*

Find the measure of ∠*DEF*.

SOLUTION

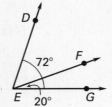

$m\angle DEG = m\angle DEF + m\angle FEG$	Angle Addition Postulate
$72° = m\angle DEF + 20°$	Substitute 72° for $m\angle DEG$ and 20° for $m\angle FEG$.
$52° = m\angle DEF$	Subtract 20° from each side.

The measure of ∠*DEF* is 52°.

Exercises for Example 4

Find the measure of ∠ABD.

8.

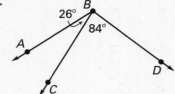

9.

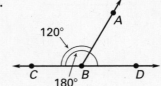

Geometry, Concepts and Skills
Practice Workbook with Examples

NAME _____ DATE _____

Reteaching with Practice

For use with pages 53–59

CALIFORNIA
Geometry Content Standards
16.0

GOAL Bisect a segment. Find the coordinates of the midpoint of a segment.

VOCABULARY

The **midpoint** of a segment is the point on the segment that divides it into two congruent segments.

A **segment bisector** is a segment, ray, line, or plane that intersects a segment at its midpoint. To **bisect** a segment means to divide the segment into two congruent segments.

The Midpoint Formula:

Words: The coordinates of the midpoint of a segment are the averages of the x-coordinates and the y-coordinates of the endpoints.

Symbols: The midpoint of the segment joining $A(x_1, y_1)$ and $B(x_2, y_2)$ is

$$\left(\frac{x_1 + x_2}{2}, \frac{y_1 + y_2}{2} \right).$$

EXAMPLE 1 *Find Segment Lengths*

Line ℓ bisects $\overline{CD}$. Find CM and CD.

SOLUTION

M is the midpoint of $\overline{CD}$, so $CM = MD$. Therefore, $CM = 12$.

You know that CD is twice the length of $\overline{MD}$.

$CD = 2 \cdot MD = 2 \cdot 12 = 24$

So, $CM = 12$ and $CD = 24$.

Exercises for Example 1

Line ℓ bisects the segment. Find the value of x.

1.   2.

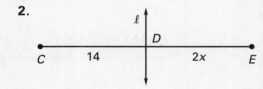

Reteaching with Practice

For use with pages 53–59

3.

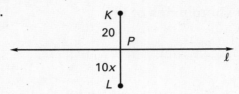

4.

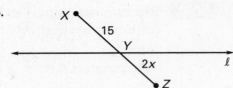

EXAMPLE 2 *Use Algebra with Segment Lengths*

M is the midpoint of $\overline{CD}$.
Find the value of x.

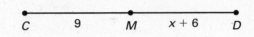

SOLUTION

$CM = MD$	M is the midpoint of $\overline{CD}$.
$9 = x + 6$	Substitute 9 for CM and $x + 6$ for MD.
$9 - 6 = x + 6 - 6$	Subtract 6 from each side.
$3 = x$	Simplify.

Exercises for Example 2

M is the midpoint of the segment. Find the segment lengths.

5. Find AM and MB.

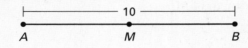

6. Find ML and KL.

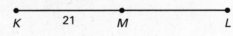

7. Find ST and SM.

8. Find CM and MD.

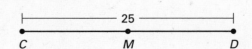

Geometry, Concepts and Skills
Practice Workbook with Examples

NAME _____ DATE _____

Reteaching with Practice

For use with pages 53–59

EXAMPLE 3 *Use the Midpoint Formula*

Find the coordinates of the midpoint of $\overline{CD}$.

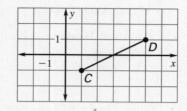

SOLUTION

Let $(x_1, y_1) = (1, -1)$ and $(x_2, y_2) = (5, 1)$.

$$M = \left(\frac{x_1 + x_2}{2}, \frac{y_1 + y_2}{2}\right) = \left(\frac{1 + 5}{2}, \frac{-1 + 1}{2}\right) = (3, 0)$$

Exercises for Example 3

Sketch $\overline{CD}$. Then find the coordinates of its midpoint.

9. $C(2, 2), D(4, 8)$ **10.** $C(-5, 4), D(1, -2)$ **11.** $C(2, -3), D(3, -7)$

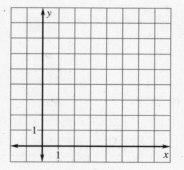 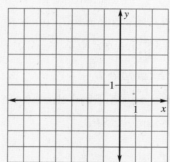 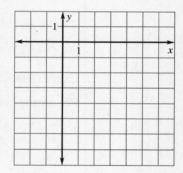

NAME_____ DATE _____

Reteaching with Practice

For use with pages 60–66

CALIFORNIA
Geometry Content Standards
1.0

GOAL Bisect an angle.

VOCABULARY

An **angle bisector** is a ray that divides an angle into two angles that are congruent.

EXAMPLE 1 *Find Angle Measures*

$\overrightarrow{QR}$ bisects $\angle PQS$, and $m\angle PQS = 62°$.
Find $m\angle PQR$ and $m\angle RQS$.

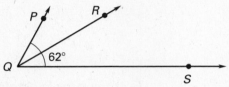

SOLUTION

$m\angle PQR = \frac{1}{2}(m\angle PQS)$ $\overrightarrow{QR}$ bisects $\angle PQS$.

$\qquad = \frac{1}{2}(62°)$ Substitute 62° for $m\angle PQS$.

$\qquad = 31°$ Simplify.

$\angle PQR$ and $\angle RQS$ are congruent, so $m\angle RQS = m\angle PQR = 31°$.

So, $m\angle PQR = 31°$ and $m\angle RQS = 31°$.

Exercises for Example 1

⋯⋯⋯⋯⋯⋯⋯⋯⋯⋯⋯⋯⋯⋯⋯⋯⋯⋯⋯⋯⋯⋯⋯⋯⋯⋯⋯⋯⋯⋯⋯⋯⋯⋯

$\overrightarrow{PS}$ **bisects the angle. Find the angle measures.**

1. Find $m\angle APS$ and $m\angle SPB$.

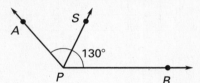

2. Find $m\angle CPS$ and $m\angle DPS$.

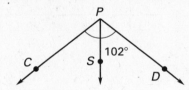

NAME_____ DATE _____

Reteaching with Practice

For use with pages 60–66

3. Find *m∠EPS* and *m∠SPF*.

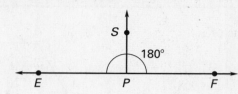

4. Find *m∠GPS* and *m∠HPS*.

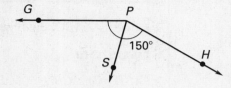

EXAMPLE 2   *Find Angle Measures and Classify an Angle*

$\overrightarrow{BD}$ bisects ∠*ABC*, and *m∠ABD* = 45°.

a. Find *m∠CBD* and *m∠ABC*.

b. Determine whether ∠*ABC* is *acute*, *right*, *obtuse*, or *straight*. Explain.

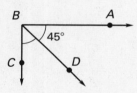

SOLUTION

a. $\overrightarrow{BD}$ bisects ∠*ABC*, so *m∠CBD* = *m∠ABD*.
You know that *m∠ABD* = 45°.
Therefore, *m∠CBD* = 45°.
The measure of ∠*ABC* is twice the measure of ∠*ABD*.
m∠ABC = 2 · (*m∠ABD*) = 2 · (45°) = 90°
So, *m∠CBD* = 45° and *m∠ABC* = 90°.

b. ∠*ABC* is a right angle because its measure is 90°.

Exercises for Example 2

$\overrightarrow{BD}$ bisects ∠*ABC*. Find *m∠CBD* and *m∠ABC*. Then determine whether ∠*ABC* is *acute, right, obtuse,* or *straight.*

5.

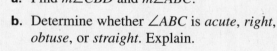

6.

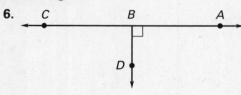

Reteaching with Practice

For use with pages 60–66

EXAMPLE 3 *Use Algebra with Angle Measures*

$\overrightarrow{BD}$ bisects $\angle ABC$. Find the value of x.

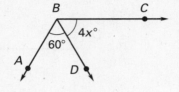

SOLUTION

$m\angle ABD = m\angle CBD$	$\overrightarrow{BD}$ bisects $\angle ABC$.
$60° = 4x°$	Substitute given measures.
$15 = x$	Divide each side by 4.

Exercises for Example 3

$\overrightarrow{BD}$ bisects $\angle ABC$. Find the value of x.

7.
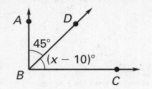

8.
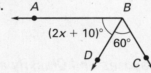

9.
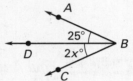

Geometry, Concepts and Skills
Practice Workbook with Examples

NAME_____ DATE _____

Reteaching with Practice

For use with pages 67–73

CALIFORNIA
Geometry Content Standards
13.0

GOAL Find measures of complementary and supplementary angles.

VOCABULARY

Two angles are **complementary angles** if the sum of their measures is 90°. Each angle is the **complement** of the other.

Two angles are **supplementary angles** if the sum of their measures is 180°. Each angle is the **supplement** of the other.

Two angles are **adjacent angles** if they share a common vertex and side, but have no common interior points.

A **theorem** is a true statement that follows from other true statements.

Theorem 2.1   Congruent Complements Theorem
If two angles are complementary to the same angle, then they are congruent.

Theorem 2.2   Congruent Supplements Theorem
If two angles are supplementary to the same angle, then they are congruent.

EXAMPLE 1 *Identify Complements and Supplements*

Determine whether the angles are *complementary*, *supplementary*, or *neither*.

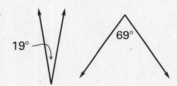

a. 61° 119°   b. 19° 69°

SOLUTION

a. Because 61° + 119° = 180°, the angles are supplementary.

b. Because 19° + 69° = 88°, the angles are neither complementary nor supplementary.

Exercises for Example 1

Determine whether the angles are *complementary, supplementary,* or *neither.*

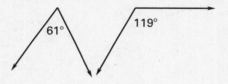

1. 54° 36°   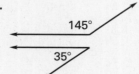 2. 145° 35°   3. 100° 105°

Reteaching with Practice

For use with pages 67–73

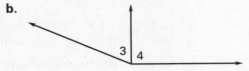

EXAMPLE 2 *Identify Adjacent Angles*

Tell whether the numbered angles are *adjacent* or *nonadjacent*.

a.
b.

SOLUTION

a. Although ∠1 and ∠2 share a common vertex, they do not share a common side. Therefore, ∠1 and ∠2 are nonadjacent.

b. Because ∠3 and ∠4 share a common vertex and side, and do not have any common interior points, ∠3 and ∠4 are adjacent.

Exercises for Example 2

Tell whether the numbered angles are *adjacent* or *nonadjacent*.

4.

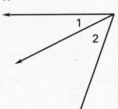

5.

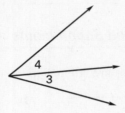

6.

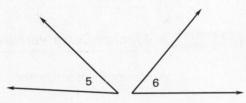

Geometry, Concepts and Skills
Practice Workbook with Examples

Reteaching with Practice

For use with pages 67–73

EXAMPLE 3 *Measures of Complements and Supplements*

    a. $\angle A$ is a supplement of $\angle B$, and $m\angle B = 42°$. Find $m\angle A$.

    b. $\angle C$ is a complement of $\angle D$, and $m\angle C = 42°$. Find $m\angle D$.

SOLUTION

a. $\angle A$ and $\angle B$ are supplements, so their sum is $180°$.

$$m\angle A + m\angle B = 180°$$
$$m\angle A + 42° = 180°$$
$$m\angle A + 42° - 42° = 180° - 42°$$
$$m\angle A = 138°$$

b. $\angle C$ and $\angle D$ are complements, so their sum is $90°$.

$$m\angle C + m\angle D = 90°$$
$$42° + m\angle D = 90°$$
$$42° + m\angle D - 42° = 90° - 42°$$
$$m\angle D = 48°$$

Exercises for Example 3

Find the angle measure.

7. $\angle A$ is a complement of $\angle B$, and $m\angle A = 11°$. Find $m\angle B$.

8. $\angle A$ is a supplement of $\angle B$, and $m\angle B = 122°$. Find $m\angle A$.

9. $\angle C$ is a complement of $\angle D$, and $m\angle C = 88°$. Find $m\angle D$.

NAME_____ DATE _____

Reteaching with Practice

For use with pages 74–81

CALIFORNIA
Geometry Content Standards

13.0

GOAL Find measures of angles formed by intersecting lines.

VOCABULARY

Two angles are **vertical angles** if they are not adjacent and their sides are formed by two intersecting lines.

Two adjacent angles are a **linear pair** if their noncommon sides are on the same line.

Postulate 7   Linear Pair Postulate
If two angles form a linear pair, then they are supplementary.

Theorem 2.3   Vertical Angles Theorem
Vertical angles are congruent.

EXAMPLE 1 *Identify Vertical Angles and Linear Pairs*

Determine whether the labeled angles are *vertical angles*, a *linear pair*, or *neither*.

a.   b. 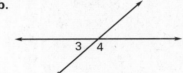   c.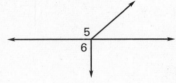

SOLUTION

a. ∠1 and ∠2 are vertical angles because they are not adjacent and their sides are formed by two intersecting lines.

b. ∠3 and ∠4 are a linear pair because they are adjacent and their noncommon sides are on the same line.

c. ∠5 and ∠6 are neither vertical angles nor a linear pair.

Exercises for Example 1

Determine whether the labeled angles are *vertical angles*, a *linear pair*, or *neither*.

1.   2.   3.

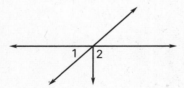   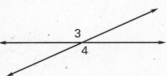   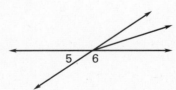

Geometry, Concepts and Skills
Practice Workbook with Examples

NAME _____ DATE _____

Reteaching with Practice

For use with pages 74–81

EXAMPLE 2 *Use the Linear Pair Postulate*

Find the measure of ∠1.

SOLUTION

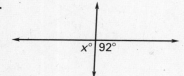

The angles are a linear pair.
By the Linear Pair Postulate,
they are supplementary.

$m\angle 1 + 148° = 180°$ Definition of supplementary angles.

$m\angle 1 = 32°$ Subtract 148° from each side.

Exercises for Example 2

Find the value of *x*.

4.

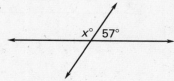

5.

6.

NAME_____ DATE _____

Reteaching with Practice

For use with pages 74–81

EXAMPLE 3 ***Use the Vertical Angles Theorem***

Find the measure of ∠ABE.

SOLUTION

∠DBC and ∠ABE are vertical angles.
By the Vertical Angles Theorem,
∠DBC ≅ ∠ABE, so
m∠DBC = m∠ABE = 82°.

Exercises for Example 3

....

Find the value of the variable.

7.

8.

9.

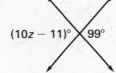

10.

Reteaching with Practice

For use with pages 82–87

CALIFORNIA
Geometry Content Standards
3.0

GOAL Use if-then statements. Apply laws of logic.

VOCABULARY

An **if-then statement** has two parts. The "if" part contains the **hypothesis.** The "then" part contains the **conclusion.**

Deductive reasoning uses facts, definitions, accepted properties, and the laws of logic to make a logical argument.

Laws of Logic

Law of Detachment
If the hypothesis of a true if-then statement is true, then the conclusion is also true.

Law of Syllogism
If *statement p*, then *statement q*.
If *statement q*, then *statement r*.   If these statements are true,

If *statement p*, then *statement r*. ◄——   then this statement is true.

EXAMPLE 1 *Identify the Hypothesis and Conclusion*

Identify the hypothesis and the conclusion of the if-then statement.

If I do my chores, then I will be given my allowance.

SOLUTION

"I do my chores" is the hypothesis.

"I will be given my allowance" is the conclusion.

Exercises for Example 1

Identify the hypothesis and the conclusion of the statement.

1. If it is raining outside, then there are clouds in the sky.

2. If two angles are vertical angles, then the two angles are congruent.

Reteaching with Practice

For use with pages 82–87

EXAMPLE 2 *Write If-Then Statements*

Rewrite the statement as an if-then statement.

a. I will get a B in History class if I get an A on the final exam in that class.

b. A right angle measures 90°.

SOLUTION

a. If I get an A on the final exam in History class, I will get a B in that class.

b. If an angle is a right angle, then the angle measures 90°.

Exercises for Example 2

Rewrite the statement as an if-then statement.

3. An even number is divisible by two.

4. The measures of two angles are equal if the two angles are congruent.

EXAMPLE 3 *Use the Law of Detachment*

Which argument is correct?

Argument 1: If two angles measure 115° and 65°, then the angles are supplementary. $\angle 1$ and $\angle 2$ are supplementary. So, $m\angle 1 = 115°$ and $m\angle 2 = 65°$.

Argument 2: If two angles measure 115° and 65°, then the angles are supplementary. The measure of $\angle 1$ is 115° and the measure of $\angle 2$ is 65°. So, $\angle 1$ and $\angle 2$ are supplementary.

SOLUTION

Argument 2 is correct. The hypothesis (two angles measure 115° and 65°) is true, which implies that the conclusion (they are supplementary) is true by the Law of Detachment.

Reteaching with Practice

For use with pages 82–87

Exercise for Example 3

Determine which argument is correct. Explain your reasoning.

5. *Argument 1:* If it is noon on Monday, then the children are in school. The children are in school. So, it is noon on Monday.

   Argument 2: If it is noon on Monday, then the children are in school. It is noon on Monday. So, the children are in school.

EXAMPLE 4 *Use the Law of Syllogism*

Write the statement that follows from the pair of true statements.

If the juice is knocked over, then it will spill on the carpet.
If the juice spills on the carpet, then it will stain the carpet.

SOLUTION

Use the Law of Syllogism. If the juice is knocked over, then it will stain the carpet.

Exercise for Example 4

Write the statement that follows from the pair of true statements.

6. If I throw the stick, then my dog will go fetch it.
   If my dog fetches the stick, then he will bring it back to me.

Reteaching with Practice

For use with pages 88–94

CALIFORNIA
Geometry Content Standards
4.0

GOAL Use properties of equality and congruence.

VOCABULARY

Properties of Equality and Congruence
Reflexive Property
Equality: $AB = AB$ **Congruence**: $\overline{AB} \cong \overline{AB}$
          $m\angle A = m\angle A$ $\angle A \cong \angle A$

Symmetric Property
Equality: If $AB = CD$, then $CD = AB$.   **Congruence:** If $\overline{AB} \cong \overline{CD}$, then $\overline{CD} \cong \overline{AB}$.
        If $m\angle A = m\angle B$, then $m\angle B = m\angle A$.   If $\angle A \cong \angle B$, then $\angle B \cong \angle A$.

Transitive Property
Equality: If $AB = CD$ and $CD = EF$,   **Congruence:** If $\overline{AB} \cong \overline{CD}$ and $\overline{CD} \cong \overline{EF}$,
        then $AB = EF$.   then $\overline{AB} \cong \overline{EF}$.
        If $m\angle A = m\angle B$ and $m\angle B = m\angle C$,   If $\angle A \cong \angle B$ and $\angle B \cong \angle C$,
        then $m\angle A = m\angle C$.   then $\angle A \cong \angle C$.

Properties of Equality
Addition Property
Adding the same number to each side of an equation produces an equivalent equation.

Subtraction Property
Subtracting the same number from each side of an equation produces an equivalent equation.

Multiplication Property
Multiplying each side of an equation by the same nonzero number produces an equivalent equation.

Division Property
Dividing each side of an equation by the same nonzero number produces an equivalent equation.

Substitution Property
Substituting a number for a variable in an equation produces an equivalent equation.

EXAMPLE 1 *Name Properties of Equality and Congruence*

Name the property that the statement illustrates.

a. $\overline{ST} \cong \overline{ST}$

b. If $m\angle R = m\angle S$ and $m\angle S = m\angle T$, then $m\angle R = m\angle T$.

c. If $AB = EF$, then $EF = AB$.

SOLUTION

a. Reflexive Property of Congruence

b. Transitive Property of Equality

c. Symmetric Property of Equality

NAME _____ DATE _____

Reteaching with Practice

For use with pages 88–94

Exercises for Example 1

Name the property that the statement illustrates.

1. If $\overline{MN} \cong \overline{OP}$ and $\overline{OP} \cong \overline{QR}$, then $\overline{MN} \cong \overline{QR}$

2. If $\angle G \cong \angle Z$, then $\angle Z \cong \angle G$.

EXAMPLE 2 *Use Properties of Equality*

In the diagram, $\angle 1$ and $\angle 2$ are a linear
pair and $m\angle 1 = m\angle 3$. Show that
$m\angle 2 + m\angle 3 = 180°$.

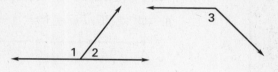

SOLUTION

$m\angle 2 + m\angle 1 = 180°$	Linear Pair Postulate
$m\angle 1 = m\angle 3$	Given
$m\angle 2 + m\angle 3 = 180°$	Substitution Property of Equality

Exercise for Example 2

In the diagram, $\overrightarrow{AC}$ bisects $\angle BAD$ and $\overrightarrow{AD}$ bisects $\angle CAE$.
Complete the argument to show that $\angle BAC \cong \angle DAE$.

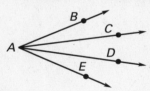

3. $\angle BAC \cong \angle CAD$ Definition of _____

    $\angle CAD \cong \angle DAE$ Definition of _____

    $\angle BAC \cong \angle DAE$ _____ Property of _____

NAME _____ DATE _____

Reteaching with Practice

For use with pages 88–94

EXAMPLE 3 *Use Algebra*

Find the value of x, given that
$EF = FG$ and $FG = GH$.

$$\overset{\bullet}{E} \underset{}{\,4x + 3\,} \overset{\bullet}{F} \qquad \overset{\bullet}{G} \quad 23 \quad \overset{\bullet}{H}$$

SOLUTION

$EF = GH$	Transitive Property of Equality
$4x + 3 = 23$	Substitute $(4x + 3)$ for EF and 23 for GH.
$4x = 20$	Subtract 3 from each side.
$x = 5$	Divide each side by 4.

Exercise for Example 3

Find the value of the variable.

4. $AB = BC, BC = CD$

$$\overset{\bullet}{A} \quad 20 \quad \overset{\bullet}{B} \qquad \overset{\bullet}{C}\,7x - 1\,\overset{\bullet}{D}$$

Reteaching with Practice

For use with pages 107–113

GOAL Identify relationships between lines.

VOCABULARY

Two lines are **parallel lines** if they lie in the same plane and do not intersect.

Two lines are **perpendicular lines** if they intersect to form a right angle.

Two lines are **skew lines** if they do not lie in the same plane and do not intersect.

Two planes are **parallel planes** if they do not intersect.

A **line perpendicular to a plane** is a line that intersects a plane in a point and that is perpendicular to every line in the plane that intersects it.

EXAMPLE 1 *Identify Parallel and Perpendicular Lines*

Determine whether the lines are *parallel*, *perpendicular*, or *neither*.

a. t and u

b. s and t

c. r and u

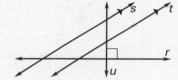

SOLUTION

a. Lines t and u intersect, so they are not parallel. Their intersection does not form a 90° angle, so they are not perpendicular. So, lines t and u are neither parallel nor perpendicular.

b. Lines s and t are parallel. Recall that triangles are used to indicate that lines are parallel.

c. Lines r and u intersect, and their intersection forms a 90° angle. So, lines r and u are perpendicular.

NAME_____ DATE _____

Reteaching with Practice

Exercises for Example 1

Determine whether the lines are *parallel*, *perpendicular*, or *neither*.

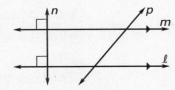

1. ℓ and m

2. m and n

3. n and p

4. ℓ and n

5. ℓ and p

EXAMPLE 2 *Identify Skew Lines*

Determine whether the lines are skew.

a. ℓ and m

b. ℓ and n

c. m and n

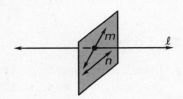

SOLUTION

a. Lines ℓ and m are not skew lines because they intersect.

b. Lines ℓ and n are skew lines because they do not lie in the same plane and they do not intersect.

c. Lines m and n are not skew lines because they lie in the same plane.

Exercises for Example 2

Determine whether the lines are skew.

6. a and b

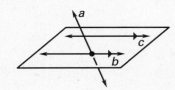

7. b and c

8. a and c

Reteaching with Practice

For use with pages 107–113

EXAMPLE 3 *Identify Relationships in Space*

a. Name a plane that appears parallel to plane *P*.

b. Name a line that is perpendicular to plane *R*.

c. Name a line that is skew to line *m*.

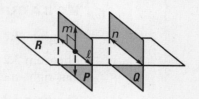

SOLUTION

a. Plane *Q* appears to be parallel to plane *P*.

b. Line *m* is perpendicular to plane *R*.

c. Line *n* is skew to line *m*.

Exercises for Example 3

Think of each segment in the diagram as part of a line.

9. Name a plane that appears parallel to plane *ABC*.

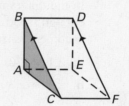

10. Name a line that is perpendicular to plane *ABD*.

11. Name a line that is perpendicular to plane *AEC*.

12. Name a line that is skew to $\overleftrightarrow{BC}$.

13. Name a line that is parallel to $\overleftrightarrow{BC}$.

Reteaching with Practice

For use with pages 114–120

GOAL Use theorems about perpendicular lines.

VOCABULARY

Theorem 3.1   All right angles are congruent.

Theorem 3.2   If two lines are perpendicular, then they intersect to form four right angles.

Theorem 3.3   If two lines intersect to form adjacent congruent angles, then the lines are perpendicular.

Theorem 3.4   If two sides of adjacent acute angles are perpendicular, then the angles are complementary.

EXAMPLE 1   *Perpendicular Lines and Reasoning*

In the diagram, $a \perp c$ and $b \perp d$. Determine whether enough information is given to conclude that the statement is true. Explain your reasoning.

a. $\angle 1 \cong \angle 2$

b. $\angle 2 \cong \angle 3$

c. $\angle 3 \cong \angle 4$

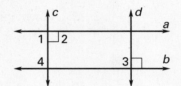

SOLUTION

a. Yes, enough information is given. Lines a and c are perpendicular. So, by Theorem 3.2, $\angle 1$ and $\angle 2$ are right angles. By Theorem 3.1, all right angles are congruent. So, $\angle 1 \cong \angle 2$.

b. Yes, enough information is given. Lines b and d are perpendicular. So, by Theorem 3.2, $\angle 3$ is a right angle. By Theorem 3.1, all right angles are congruent. So $\angle 2 \cong \angle 3$.

c. No, not enough information is given to conclude that $\angle 3 \cong \angle 4$. You know that $\angle 3$ is a right angle, but you are not given any information about $\angle 4$.

Geometry, Concepts and Skills
Practice Workbook with Examples

Reteaching with Practice

For use with pages 114–120

Exercises for Example 1
....

In the diagram, $k \perp \ell$ and $k \perp n$. Determine whether enough information is given to conclude that the statement is true. Explain your reasoning.

1. $\angle 1 \cong \angle 2$

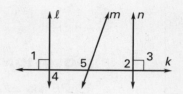

2. $\angle 2 \cong \angle 3$

3. $\angle 3 \cong \angle 4$

4. $\angle 4 \cong \angle 5$

EXAMPLE 2 *Use Theorems About Perpendicular Lines*
_____

In the diagram, $\angle RPS \cong \angle RPT$. Is $RP \perp ST$?

SOLUTION

If two lines intersect to form adjacent congruent angles, as $\overleftrightarrow{RP}$ and $\overleftrightarrow{ST}$ do, then the lines are perpendicular (Theorem 3.3). So, $\overleftrightarrow{RP} \perp \overleftrightarrow{ST}$.

Exercise for Example 2
....

5. In the diagram, $\angle GPH \cong \angle HPI$. Is $\angle GPJ$ a right angle? Explain.

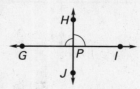

NAME_____ DATE _____

Reteaching with Practice

For use with pages 114–120

EXAMPLE 3 **Use Algebra with Perpendicular Lines**

In the diagram, $\overleftrightarrow{AC} \perp \overleftrightarrow{BD}$. Find the value of *x*.

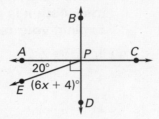

SOLUTION

$\angle APE$ and $\angle EPD$ are adjacent acute angles and $\overleftrightarrow{AC} \perp \overleftrightarrow{BD}$. So,
$\angle APE$ and $\angle EPD$ are complementary (Theorem 3.4).

$20° + (6x + 4)° = 90°$	$m\angle APE + m\angle EPD = 90°$
$6x + 24 = 90$	Simplify.
$6x = 66$	Subtract 24 from each side.
$x = 11$	Divide each side by 6.

Exercises for Example 3

Find the value of the variable.

6. $\overrightarrow{WX} \perp \overrightarrow{WZ}$

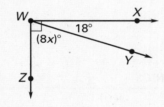

7. $\overleftrightarrow{JL} \perp \overleftrightarrow{KM}$

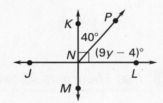

8. $\angle QTR \cong \angle RTS$

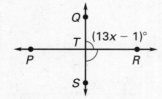

NAME _____ DATE _____

Reteaching with Practice

For use with pages 121–125

CALIFORNIA
Geometry Content Standards
7.0

GOAL Identify angles formed by transversals.

VOCABULARY

A **transversal** is a line that intersects two or more coplanar lines at different points.

When two lines are intersected by a transversal, two angles are called **corresponding angles** if they occupy corresponding positions.

When two lines are intersected by a transversal, two angles are called **alternate interior angles** if they lie between the two lines on the opposite sides of the transversal.

When two lines are intersected by a transversal, two angles are called **alternate exterior angles** if they lie outside the two lines on the opposite sides of the transversal.

When two lines are intersected by a transversal, two angles are called **same-side interior angles** if they lie between the two lines on the same side of the transversal.

EXAMPLE 1 *Describe Angles Formed by Transversals*

Describe the relationship between the numbered angles.

a. 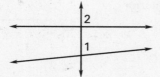   b. 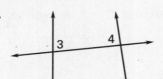   c.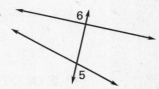

SOLUTION

a. ∠1 and ∠2 are corresponding angles.

b. ∠3 and ∠4 are same-side interior angles.

c. ∠5 and ∠6 are alternate exterior angles.

NAME_____ DATE _____

Reteaching with Practice

For use with pages 121–125

Exercises for Example 1

Describe the relationship between the numbered angles.

1.

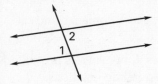

2.

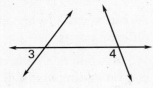

3.

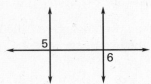

4.

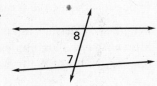

EXAMPLE 2 *Identify Angles Formed by Transversals*

List all pairs of angles that fit the description.

a. corresponding　　　　**b.** alternate interior

c. alternate exterior　　　**d.** same-side interior

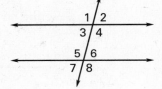

SOLUTION

a. corresponding: $\angle 1$ and $\angle 5$, $\angle 2$ and $\angle 6$, $\angle 3$ and $\angle 7$, $\angle 4$ and $\angle 8$

b. alternate interior: $\angle 3$ and $\angle 6$, $\angle 4$ and $\angle 5$

c. alternate exterior: $\angle 1$ and $\angle 8$, $\angle 2$ and $\angle 7$

d. same-side interior: $\angle 3$ and $\angle 5$, $\angle 4$ and $\angle 6$

Exercises for Example 2

List all pairs of angles that fit the description.

5. alternate exterior

6. corresponding

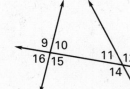

7. same-side interior

8. alternate interior

Geometry, Concepts and Skills
Practice Workbook with Examples

Reteaching with Practice

For use with pages 121–125

EXAMPLE 3 **Classify Angles Formed by Transversals**

Use the diagram to describe the relationship between
the pair of angles.

a. ∠ABC and ∠HGB   **b.** ∠EDF and ∠BGH

c. ∠BDG and ∠DGB   **d.** ∠DBG and ∠BGH

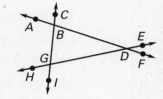

SOLUTION

The transversal is always the line containing one side of both angles.

a. corresponding   **b.** alternate exterior

c. same-side interior   **d.** alternate interior

Exercises for Example 3

**Use the diagram to describe the relationship
between the pair of angles.**

9. ∠JKP and ∠KPN

10. ∠LKM and ∠QPR

11. ∠JKL and ∠RPK

12. ∠JKP and ∠KPR

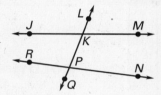

Reteaching with Practice

For use with pages 126–135

CALIFORNIA
Geometry Content Standards

7.0

GOAL Find the congruent angles formed when a transversal cuts pallel lines.

VOCABULARY

Corresponding Angles Postulate If two parallel lines are cut by a transversal, then corresponding angles are congruent.

Alternate Interior Angles Theorem If two parallel lines are cut by a transversal, then alternate interior angles are congruent.

Alternate Exterior Angles Theorem If two parallel lines are cut by a transversal, then alternate exterior angles are congruent.

Same-Side Interior Angles Theorem If two parallel lines are cut by a transversal, then same-side interior angles are supplementary.

EXAMPLE 1 *Find Measures of Corresponding Angles*

Find the measure of the numbered angle.

SOLUTION

$m\angle 1 = 110°$

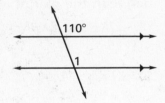

Exercises for Example 1

Find the measure of the numbered angle.

1.

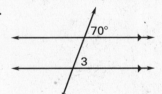

2.

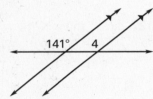

3.

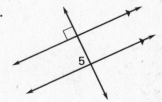

Geometry, Concepts and Skills
Practice Workbook with Examples

Reteaching with Practice

For use with pages 126–135

EXAMPLE 2 *Find Measures of Alternate Interior and Alternate Exterior Angles*

Find the measure of the numbered angle.

a.

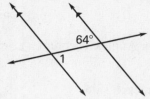

b.

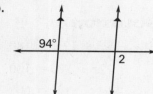

SOLUTION

a. $m\angle 1 = 64°$ **b.** $m\angle 2 = 94°$

Exercises for Example 2

Find the measure of the numbered angle.

4.

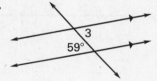

5.

6.

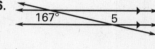

EXAMPLE 3 *Find Measures of Same-Side Interior Angles*

Find the measure of the numbered angle.

SOLUTION

$m\angle 1 + 78° = 180°$ Same-Side Interior Angles Theorem
$\quad m\angle 1 = 102°$ Subtract 78° from each side.

Exercises for Example 3

Find the measure of the numbered angle.

7.

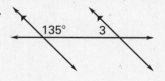

8.

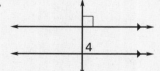

9.

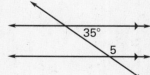

Reteaching with Practice

EXAMPLE 4 *Use Algebra with Angle Relationships*

Find the value of *x*.

SOLUTION

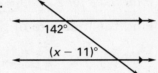

$(12x - 5)° + 125° = 180°$	Same-Side Interior Angles Theorem
$12x + 120 = 180$	Simplify.
$12x = 60$	Subtract 120 from each side.
$x = 5$	Divide each side by 12.

Exercises for Example 4

Find the value of *x*.

10.

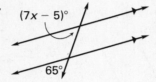

$(7x - 5)°$

$65°$

11.

$142°$

$(x - 11)°$

NAME _____ DATE _____

Reteaching with Practice

For use with pages 136–142

GOAL Show that two lines are parallel.

VOCABULARY

The **converse** of an if-then statement is the statement formed by switching the hypothesis and the conclusion.

Corresponding Angles Converse If two lines are cut by a transversal so that corresponding angles are congruent, then the lines are parallel.

Alternate Interior Angles Converse If two lines are cut by a transversal so that alternate interior angles are congruent, then the lines are parallel.

Alternate Exterior Angles Converse If two lines are cut by a transversal so that alternate exterior angles are congruent, then the lines are parallel.

Same-Side Interior Angles Converse If two lines are cut by a transversal so that same-side interior angles are supplementary, then the lines are parallel.

EXAMPLE 1 *Write the Converse of an If-Then Statement*

Statement: If two angles are a linear pair, then the sum of their measures is 180°.

a. Write the converse of the true statement above.

b. Determine whether the converse is true.

SOLUTION

a. *Converse*: If the sum of the measures of two angles is 180°, then the angles are a linear pair.

b. The converse is false. Consider an instance where one angle has a measure of 100° and a second angle has a measure of 80°, but the two angles are not adjacent. In this instance, the sum of the measures of the two angles is 180°, but the angles are not a linear pair.

NAME_____ DATE _____

Reteaching with Practice

For use with pages 136–142

Exercises for Example 1

Write the converse of the true statement. Then determine whether the converse is true.

1. If the measure of an angle is between 0° and 90°, then the angle is acute.

2. If ∠1 and ∠2 are vertical angles, then ∠1 ≅ ∠2.

3. If line ℓ is perpendicular to plane *P*, then ℓ intersects *P* in a point and is perpendicular to every line in *P* that intersects it.

EXAMPLE 2 *Use Corresponding Angles Converse*

Is enough information given to conclude that *m* ∥ *k*? Explain.

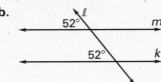

a.

b.

SOLUTION

a. No. You are not given any information about the angles formed where
ℓ and *k* intersect. You would need this information to use the
Corresponding Angles Converse.

b. Yes. The two marked angles are corresponding and congruent. There is enough
information to use the Corresponding Angles Converse to conclude that *m* ∥ *k*.

Geometry, Concepts and Skills
Practice Workbook with Examples

NAME_____ DATE _____

Reteaching with Practice

Exercises for Example 2

Is enough information given to conclude that *r* ∥ *s*? Explain.

4.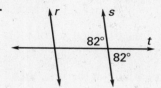

5.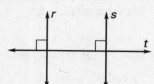

EXAMPLE 3 *Identify Parallel Lines*

Does the diagram give enough information to conclude that *a* ∥ *b*? Explain.

a.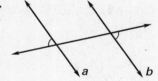

b.

SOLUTION

a. No. Not enough information is given to conclude that *a* ∥ *b*.

b. Yes. The angle congruence marks on the diagram allow you to conclude that *a* ∥ *b* by the Alternate Exterior Angles Converse.

Exercises for Example 3

Does the diagram give enough information to conclude that *a* ∥ *b*? Explain.

6.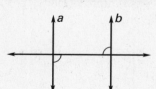

7.

Reteaching with Practice

For use with pages 143–151

CALIFORNIA
Geometry Content Standards
7.0

GOAL Construct parallel and perpendicular lines.
Use properties of parallel and perpendicular lines.

VOCABULARY

A **construction** is a geometric drawing that uses a limited set of tools, usually a compass and a straightedge.

Parallel Postulate If there is a line and a point not on the line, then there is exactly one line through the point parallel to the given line.

Perpendicular Postulate If there is a line and a point not on the line, then there is exactly one line through the point perpendicular to the given line.

Theorem 3.11 If two lines are parallel to the same line, then they are parallel to each other.

Theorem 3.12 In a plane, if two lines are perpendicular to the same line, then they are parallel to each other.

EXAMPLE 1 *Construct a Perpendicular Line*

Construct a line that passes through point *R* and is perpendicular to line *n*.

SOLUTION

1. Draw an arc with center *R* that intersects *n* twice. Label the intersections *G* and *H*.

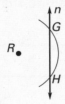

2. Draw an arc with center *G*. Using the same radius, draw an arc with center *H*. Label the intersection of the arcs *S*.

3. Use a straightedge to draw $\overleftrightarrow{RS}$, $\overleftrightarrow{RS} \perp n$.

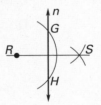

Geometry, Concepts and Skills
Practice Workbook with Examples

Reteaching with Practice

For use with pages 143–151

Exercises for Example 1

1. Draw a vertical line *a* and a point *G* to the left of the line. Construct a line *b* that passes through point *G* and is perpendicular to *a*.

2. Draw a vertical line *c* and a point *H* to the right of the line. Construct a line *d* that passes through point *H* and is parallel to *c*.

EXAMPLE 2 *Use Properties of Parallel Lines*

In the diagram, $k \parallel n$, $n \parallel m$, and $m \parallel \ell$.
Explain why $k \parallel \ell$.

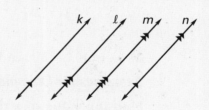

SOLUTION

You are given that $k \parallel n$ and $n \parallel m$. By Theorem 3.11, $k \parallel m$. You are also given that $m \parallel \ell$. Using Theorem 3.11 again, you can conclude that $k \parallel \ell$.

NAME_____ DATE _____

Reteaching with Practice

For use with pages 143–151

Exercises for Example 2

Using the given information, explain why *a* ∥ *c*.

3. $a \parallel b, b \parallel c$

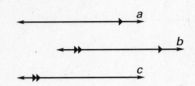

4. $\angle 1 \cong \angle 2, b \parallel c$

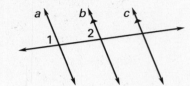

EXAMPLE 3 *Use Properties of Parallel Lines*

Find the value of *x* that makes $\overleftrightarrow{WX} \parallel \overleftrightarrow{YZ}$.

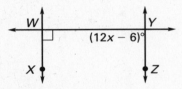

SOLUTION

By Theorem 3.12, $\overleftrightarrow{WX}$ and $\overleftrightarrow{YZ}$ will be parallel if $\overleftrightarrow{WX}$ and $\overleftrightarrow{YZ}$ are both perpendicular to $\overleftrightarrow{WY}$. For this to be true $\angle WYZ$ must measure 90°.

$$(12x - 6)° = 90° \qquad m\angle WYZ \text{ must be } 90°.$$
$$12x = 96 \qquad \text{Add 6 to each side.}$$
$$x = 8 \qquad \text{Divide each side by 12.}$$

Answer: If $x = 8$, then $\overleftrightarrow{WX} \parallel \overleftrightarrow{YZ}$.

Exercises for Example 3

Find the value of *x* that makes *m* ∥ *n*.

5.

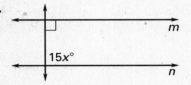

6.

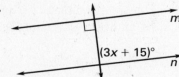

NAME _____ DATE _____

Reteaching with Practice

For use with pages 152–159

CALIFORNIA
Geometry Content Standards
22.0

GOAL Identify and use translations.

VOCABULARY

A **transformation** is an operation that maps, or moves, a figure onto a new figure.

The new figure after the transformation is called the **image.**

A **translation** is a transformation in which the image is created by sliding the original figure.

EXAMPLE 1 *Compare a Figure and Its Image*

Decide whether the white figure is a translation of the shaded figure.

a.

b.

c.

SOLUTION

a. No, this is not a translation. The original figure is rotated to get the image.

b. Yes, this is a translation.

c. No, this is not a translation. The original figure has been shrunk to get the image.

Exercises for Example 1
· ·

Decide whether the white figure is a translation of the shaded figure.

1.

2.

3.

NAME_____ DATE _____

Reteaching with Practice

For use with pages 152–159

EXAMPLE 2 *Describe Translations*

Describe the translation of the segment.

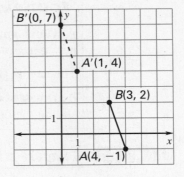

SOLUTION

Point *A* is moved 3 units to the left and 5 units up to get point *A'*. So every point on $\overline{AB}$ moves 3 units to the left and 5 units up.

Exercises for Example 2

Describe the translation of the figure.

4.

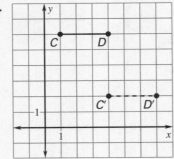

5.

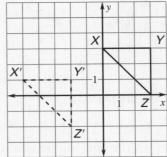

Reteaching with Practice

For use with pages 150–159

EXAMPLE 3 **Use Coordinate Notation**

Describe the translation using coordinate notation.

SOLUTION

Each point is moved 1 unit to the right and 5 units up.
The translation can be described using the notation
$(x, y) \rightarrow (x + 1, y + 5)$.

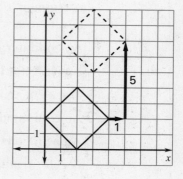

Exercises for Example 3

Describe the translation using coordinate notation.

6.

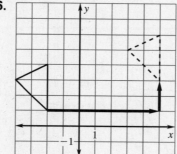

7.

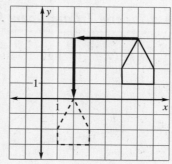

NAME_____ DATE _____

Reteaching with Practice

For use with pages 173–178

CALIFORNIA
Geometry Content Standards
12.0

GOAL **Classify triangles by their sides and by their angles.**

VOCABULARY

A **triangle** is a figure formed by three segments joining three noncollinear points.

An **equilateral triangle** has three congruent sides.

An **isosceles triangle** has at least two congruent sides.

A **scalene triangle** has no congruent sides.

An **equiangular triangle** has three congruent angles.

An **acute triangle** has three acute angles.

A **right triangle** has one right angle.

An **obtuse triangle** has one obtuse angle.

A **vertex** of a triangle is a point that joins two sides of the triangle.

EXAMPLE 1 *Classify Triangles by Sides*

Classify the triangle by its sides.

a.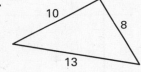

b.

c.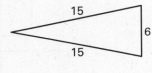

SOLUTION

a. Because this triangle has no congruent sides, it is scalene.

b. Because this triangle has three congruent sides, it is equilateral.

c. Because this triangle has two congruent sides, it is isosceles.

Geometry, Concepts and Skills
Practice Workbook with Examples

NAME_____ DATE _____

Reteaching with Practice

For use with pages 173–178

Exercises for Example 1

Classify the triangle by its sides.

1.

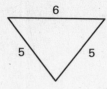

2.

3.

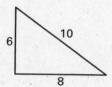

4.

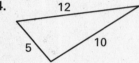

EXAMPLE 2 *Classify Triangles by Angles*

Classify the triangle by its angles.

a.

b.

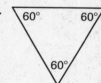

c.

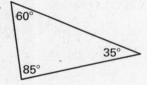

SOLUTION

a. Because this triangle has a right angle, it is a right triangle.

b. Because this triangle has three congruent angles, it is an equiangular triangle.

c. Because this triangle has three angles with measures less than 90°, it is an acute triangle.

NAME _____ DATE _____

Reteaching with Practice

For use with pages 173–178

Exercises for Example 2

Classify the triangle by its angles.

5.

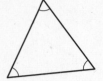

6.

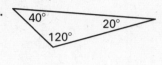
40° 20° 120°

7.

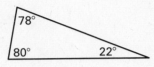
78° 80° 22°

EXAMPLE 3 *Identify the Parts of a Triangle*

Name the side that is opposite the angle.

a. ∠X   **b.** ∠Y   **c.** ∠Z

SOLUTION

a. $\overline{YZ}$ is the side that is opposite ∠X.

b. $\overline{XZ}$ is the side that is opposite ∠Y.

c. $\overline{XY}$ is the side that is opposite ∠Z.

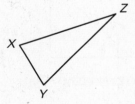

Exercises for Example 3

Name the side that is opposite the angle.

8. ∠J

9. ∠K

10. ∠L

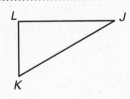

Geometry, Concepts and Skills
Practice Workbook with Examples

Reteaching with Practice

For use with pages 179–184

CALIFORNIA
Geometry Content Standards

12.0

GOAL **Find angle measures in triangles.**

VOCABULARY

A **corollary** to a theorem is a statement that can be proved easily using the theorem.

When the sides of a triangle are extended, the three original angles are called **interior angles**. The angles that are adjacent to the interior angles are called **exterior angles**.

Theorem 4.1   Triangle Sum Theorem
The sum of the measures of the angles of a triangle is 180°.

Corollary to the Triangle Sum Theorem
The acute angles of a right triangle are complementary.

Theorem 4.2   Exterior Angle Theorem
The measure of an exterior angle of a triangle is equal to the sum of the measures of the two nonadjacent interior angles.

EXAMPLE 1   *Find an Angle Measure*

Given $m\angle D = 75°$ and $m\angle F = 61°$, find $m\angle E$.

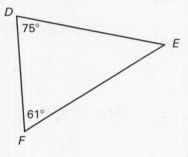

SOLUTION

$m\angle D + m\angle E + m\angle F = 180°$	Triangle Sum Theorem
$75° + m\angle E + 61° = 180°$	Substitute 75° for $m\angle D$ and 61° for $m\angle F$.
$136° + m\angle E = 180°$	Simplify.
$136° + m\angle E - 136° = 180° - 136°$	Subtract 136° from each side.
$m\angle E = 44°$	Simplify.

Reteaching with Practice

For use with pages 179–184

Exercises for Example 1

Find m∠A.

1.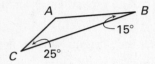

2.

3.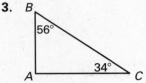

EXAMPLE 2 *Find an Angle Measure*

△ *DEF* is a right triangle and m∠D = 52°.
Find m∠F.

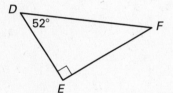

SOLUTION

$m\angle D + m\angle F = 90°$	Corollary to the Triangle Sum Theorem
$52° + m\angle F = 90°$	Substitute 52° for $m\angle D$.
$52° + m\angle F - 52° = 90° - 52°$	Subtract 52° from each side.
$m\angle F = 38°$	Simplify.

Exercises for Example 2

△ **ABC is a right triangle. Find m∠A.**

4.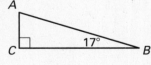

5.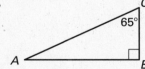

6.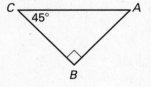

Geometry, Concepts and Skills
Practice Workbook with Examples

NAME _____ DATE _____

Reteaching with Practice
For use with pages 179–184

EXAMPLE 3 **Find an Angle Measure**

Given $m\angle D = 49°$ and $m\angle EFG = 101°$, find $m\angle E$.

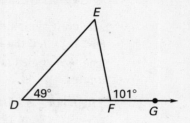

SOLUTION

$m\angle EFG = m\angle D + m\angle E$	Exterior Angle Theorem
$101° = 49° + m\angle E$	Substitute 101° for $m\angle EFG$ and 49° for $m\angle D$.
$m\angle E = 52°$	Subtract 49° from each side.

Exercises for Example 3

Find the measure of $\angle 1$.

7.

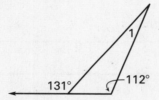

8.

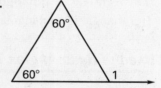

9.

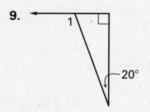

Reteaching with Practice

For use with pages 185–190

CALIFORNIA
Geometry Content Standards
12.0

GOAL Use properties of isosceles and equilateral triangles.

VOCABULARY

The congruent sides of an isosceles triangle are called **legs**. The other side is called the **base**.

The two angles at the base of an isosceles triangle are called the **base angles**.

Theorem 4.3   Base Angles Theorem

If two sides of a triangle are congruent, then the angles opposite them are congruent.

Theorem 4.4   Converse of the Base Angles Theorem

If two angles of a triangle are congruent, then the sides opposite them are congruent.

Theorem 4.5   Equilateral Theorem

If a triangle is equilateral, then it is equiangular.

Theorem 4.6   Equiangular Theorem

If a triangle is equiangular, then it is equilateral.

EXAMPLE 1   *Use the Base Angles Theorem*

Find $m\angle A$.

a.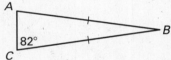

b.

SOLUTION

a. $\angle A$ is a base angle of an isosceles triangle. From the Base Angles Theorem, $\angle A$ and $\angle C$ have the same measure. So $m\angle A = 82°$.

b. $\angle B$ and $\angle C$ are base angles of an isosceles triangle. Therefore, $m\angle C = m\angle B = 67°$. Then use the Triangle Sum Theorem to find $m\angle A$.

$m\angle A + m\angle B + m\angle C = 180°$	Triangle Sum Theorem
$m\angle A + 67° + 67° = 180°$	Substitute.
$m\angle A + 134° = 180°$	Add.
$m\angle A = 46°$	Subtract 134° from each side.

Reteaching with Practice

For use with pages 185–190

Exercises for Example 1

Find $m\angle A$.

1.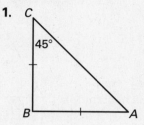

2.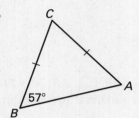

3.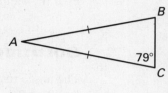

EXAMPLE 2   *Use the Converse of the Base Angles Theorem*

Find the value of x.

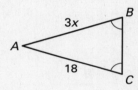

SOLUTION

By the Converse of the Base Angles Theorem, the legs have the same length.

$AB = AC$	Converse of the Base Angles Theorem
$3x = 18$	Substitute $3x$ for AB and 18 for AC.
$x = 6$	Divide each side by 3.

Exercises for Example 2

Find the value of x.

4.

5.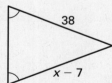

6.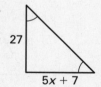

Reteaching with Practice

For use with pages 185–190

EXAMPLE 3 *Use the Equiangular Theorem*

Find the value of *x*.

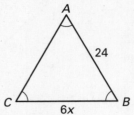

SOLUTION

The angle marks show that $\triangle ABC$ is equiangular.
So, $\triangle ABC$ is also equilateral by the Equiangular Theorem.

$$6x = 24$$ Sides of an equilateral triangle are congruent.

$$\frac{6x}{6} = \frac{24}{6}$$ Divide each side by 6.

$$x = 4$$ Simplify.

Exercises for Example 3

Find the value of x.

7.

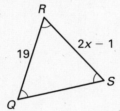

8.

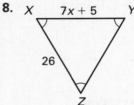

9.

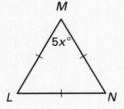

Geometry, Concepts and Skills
Practice Workbook with Examples

Reteaching with Practice

For use with pages 191–198

CALIFORNIA
Geometry Content Standards
15.0

GOAL Use the Pythagorean Theorem and the Distance Formula.

VOCABULARY

In a right triangle, the sides that form the right angle are called the **legs**. The side opposite the right angle is called the **hypotenuse**.

Theorem 4.7   The Pythagorean Theorem

In a right triangle, the square of the length of the hypotenuse is equal to the sum of the squares of the lengths of the legs.

The Distance Formula

If $A(x_1, y_1)$ and $B(x_2, y_2)$ are points in a coordinate plane, then the distance between A and B is

$$AB = \sqrt{(x_2 - x_1)^2 + (y_2 - y_1)^2}.$$

EXAMPLE 1 *Find the Length of the Hypotenuse*

Find the length of the hypotenuse.

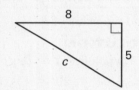

SOLUTION

$(\text{hypotenuse})^2 = (\text{leg})^2 + (\text{leg})^2$	Pythagorean Theorem
$c^2 = 8^2 + 5^2$	Substitute.
$c^2 = 64 + 25$	Evaluate exponents.
$c^2 = 89$	Add.
$\sqrt{c^2} = \sqrt{89}$	Find the positive square root.
$c \approx 9.4$	Approximate with a calculator.

Answer: The length of the hypotenuse is about 9.4.

Geometry, Concepts and Skills
Practice Workbook with Examples

67

NAME _____ DATE _____

Reteaching with Practice

For use with pages 191–198

Exercises for Example 1

Find the length of the hypotenuse. Round your answer to the nearest tenth, if necessary.

1.
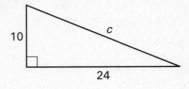

2.
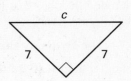

3.
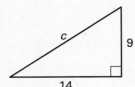

EXAMPLE 2
Find the Length of a Leg

Find the value of b.

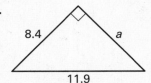

SOLUTION

$(\text{hypotenuse})^2 = (\text{leg})^2 + (\text{leg})^2$ Pythagorean Theorem

$20^2 = 15^2 + b^2$ Substitute.

$400 = 225 + b^2$ Evaluate exponents.

$175 = b^2$ Subtract.

$\sqrt{175} = \sqrt{b^2}$ Find the positive square root.

$13.2 \approx b$ Approximate with a calculator.

Exercises for Example 2

Find the unknown side length. Round your answer to the nearest tenth, if necessary.

4.
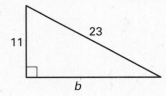

5.
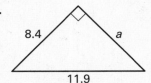

6.
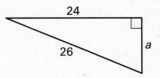

Geometry, Concepts and Skills
Practice Workbook with Examples

Reteaching with Practice

For use with pages 191–198

EXAMPLE 3 *Use the Distance Formula*

Find the distance between $K(-1, -2)$ and $L(4, 2)$.

SOLUTION

Begin by plotting the points in a coordinate plane.

$x_1 = -1, y_1 = -2, x_2 = 4, y_2 = 2$

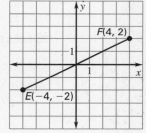

$KL = \sqrt{(x_2 - x_1)^2 + (y_2 - y_1)^2}$	Distance Formula
$KL = \sqrt{(4 - (-1))^2 + (2 - (-2))^2}$	Substitute.
$KL = \sqrt{5^2 + 4^2}$	Simplify.
$KL = \sqrt{25 + 16}$	Evaluate exponents.
$KL = \sqrt{41}$	Add.
$KL \approx 6.4$	Approximate with a calculator.

Exercises for Example 3

Find the distance between the points. Round your answer to the nearest tenth, if necessary.

7.

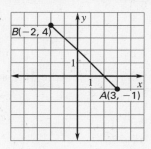

8.

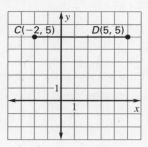

9.

NAME_____ DATE _____

Reteaching with Practice

For use with pages 199–205

CALIFORNIA
Geometry Content Standards
15.0

GOAL Use the Converse of the Pythagorean Theorem.
Use side lengths to classify triangles.

VOCABULARY

Theorem 4.8   The Converse of the Pythagorean Theorem

If the square of the length of the longest side of a triangle is equal to the sum of the squares of the lengths of the other two sides, then the triangle is a right triangle.

EXAMPLE 1 *Verify a Right Triangle*

Is $\triangle$ *EFG* a right triangle?

a.
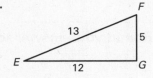

b.
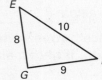

SOLUTION

Let g represent the length of the longest side of the triangle. Check to see whether the side lengths satisfy the equation $g^2 = e^2 + f^2$.

a. $g^2 \overset{?}{=} e^2 + f^2$

   $13^2 \overset{?}{=} 5^2 + 12^2$

   $169 \overset{?}{=} 25 + 144$

   $169 = 169$

   It is true that $g^2 = e^2 + f^2$, so $\triangle$ *EFG* is a right triangle.

b. $g^2 \overset{?}{=} e^2 + f^2$

   $10^2 \overset{?}{=} 9^2 + 8^2$

   $100 \overset{?}{=} 81 + 64$

   $100 \neq 145$

   It is not true that $g^2 = e^2 + f^2$, so $\triangle$ *EFG* is not a right triangle.

Geometry, Concepts and Skills
Practice Workbook with Examples

NAME_____ DATE _____

Reteaching with Practice

Exercises for Example 1

Use the Converse of the Pythagorean Theorem to determine whether △ ABC is a right triangle.

1.

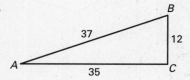

2.

3.

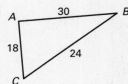

EXAMPLE 2 *Acute Triangles and Obtuse Triangles*

a. Show that the triangle
is an acute triangle.

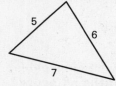

b. Show that the triangle
is an obtuse triangle.

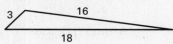

SOLUTION

Compare the side lengths.

a. $c^2 \stackrel{?}{=} a^2 + b^2$

$7^2 \stackrel{?}{=} 5^2 + 6^2$

$49 \stackrel{?}{=} 25 + 36$

$49 < 61$

Because $c^2 < a^2 + b^2$,
the triangle is acute.

b. $c^2 \stackrel{?}{=} a^2 + b^2$

$18^2 \stackrel{?}{=} 3^2 + 16^2$

$324 \stackrel{?}{=} 9 + 256$

$324 > 265$

Because $c^2 > a^2 + b^2$,
the triangle is obtuse.

NAME_____ DATE _____

Reteaching with Practice

Exercises for Example 2

4. Show that the triangle is acute.

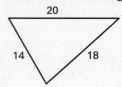

20
14   18

5. Show that the triangle is obtuse.

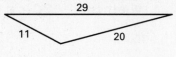

29
11   20

EXAMPLE 3 *Classify Triangles*

Classify the triangle with side lengths 6, 23, and 25 as *acute*, *right*, or *obtuse*.

SOLUTION

Compare the square of the length of the longest side with the sum of the squares of the lengths of the other two sides.

$$c^2 \stackrel{?}{=} a^2 + b^2 \qquad \text{Compare } c^2 \text{ with } a^2 + b^2.$$

$$25^2 \stackrel{?}{=} 6^2 + 23^2 \qquad \text{Substitute 25 for } c, 6 \text{ for } a, \text{ and 23 for } b.$$

$$625 \stackrel{?}{=} 36 + 529 \qquad \text{Evaluate exponents.}$$

$$625 > 565 \qquad \text{Simplify.}$$

Answer: Because $c^2 > a^2 + b^2$, the triangle is obtuse.

Exercises for Example 3

Classify the triangle with the given side lengths as *acute*, *right*, or *obtuse*.

6. 9, 12, 15   **7.** 13, 19, 24   **8.** 20, 26, 28

Reteaching with Practice

For use with pages 206–211

CALIFORNIA
Geometry Content Standards
16.0

GOAL Identify medians in triangles.

VOCABULARY

A **median of a triangle** is a segment from a vertex to the midpoint of the opposite side. The **centroid of a triangle** is the point where all three medians of the triangle intersect.

Theorem 4.9   Intersection of Medians of a Triangle

The medians of a triangle intersect at a point that is two thirds of the distance from each vertex to the midpoint of the opposite side.

EXAMPLE 1 *Draw a Median*

In △ABC, draw a median from A to its opposite side.

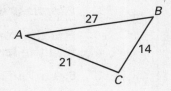

SOLUTION

The side opposite ∠ A is $\overline{BC}$. Find the midpoint of $\overline{BC}$, and label it D. Then draw a segment from point D to point A. $\overline{AD}$ is a median of △ABC.

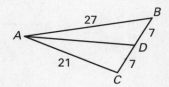

Exercises for Example 1

Draw a median from point A to its opposite side.

1.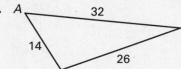

2.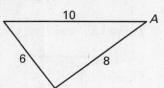

3.

4.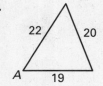

Geometry, Concepts and Skills
Practice Workbook with Examples

73

NAME _____ DATE _____

Reteaching with Practice

For use with pages 206–211

EXAMPLE 2 ## Use the Centroid of a Triangle

P is the centroid of $\triangle KLM$ and $KN = 18$.
Find KP and PN.

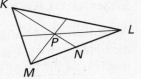

SOLUTION

Using Theorem 4.9, you know that

$$KP = \frac{2}{3}KN = \frac{2}{3}(18) = 12.$$

Now use the Segment Addition Postulate to find PN.

$KN = KP + PN$	Segment Addition Postulate
$18 = 12 + PN$	Substitute 18 for KN and 12 for KP.
$6 = PN$	Subtract 12 from each side.

A*nswer:* $\overline{KP}$ has a length of 12 and $\overline{PN}$ has a length of 6.

Exercises for Example 2

P is the centroid of the triangle. Use the given information to find the lengths.

5. Find AP and PD, given $AD = 60$.

6. Find HP and PG, given $HG = 36$.

7. Find KP and PM, given $KM = 99$.

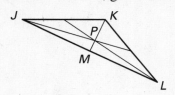

Geometry, Concepts and Skills
Practice Workbook with Examples

Reteaching with Practice

For use with pages 206–211

EXAMPLE 3 **Use the Centroid of a Triangle**

T is the centroid of $\triangle XYZ$ and $TZ = 14$.
Find SZ.

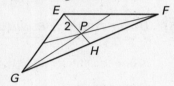

SOLUTION

$TZ = \frac{2}{3}SZ$ Use Theorem 4.9.

$14 = \frac{2}{3}SZ$ Substitute 14 for TZ.

$21 = SZ$ Multiply each side by $\frac{3}{2}$.

Answer: The median $\overline{SZ}$ has a length of 21.

Exercises for Example 3

P is the centroid of the triangle. Use the given information to find the lengths.

8. Find BD, given $BP = 8$.

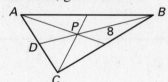

9. Find EH, given $EP = 2$.

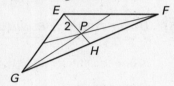

10. Find KM, given $KP = 24$.

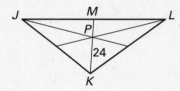

NAME_____ DATE _____

Reteaching with Practice

For use with pages 212–218

GOAL Use triangle measurements to decide which side is longest and which angle is largest.

VOCABULARY

Theorem 4.10

If one side of a triangle is longer than another side, then the angle opposite the longer side is larger than the angle opposite the shorter side.

Theorem 4.11

If one angle of a triangle is larger than another angle, then the side opposite the larger angle is longer than the side opposite the smaller angle.

Theorem 4.12   Triangle Inequality

The sum of the lengths of any two sides of a triangle is greater than the length of the third side.

EXAMPLE 1 *Order Angle Measures*

Name the smallest angle and the largest angle of △*ABC*.

SOLUTION

$AC > BC > AB$, so $m\angle B > m\angle A > m\angle C$.

$\angle C$ is the smallest angle. $\angle B$ is the largest angle.

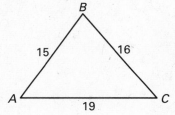

Exercises for Example 1

Name the smallest angle and the largest angle of the triangle.

1.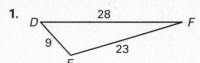

2.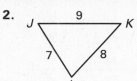

3.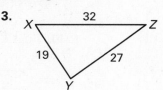

NAME_____ DATE _____

Reteaching with Practice
For use with pages 212–218

EXAMPLE 2 *Order Side Lengths*

Name the shortest side and the longest side of $\triangle ABC$.

SOLUTION

$m\angle B > m\angle A > m\angle C$, so $AC > BC > AB$.

The shortest side is $\overline{AB}$. The longest side is $\overline{AC}$.

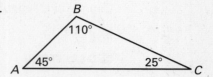

Exercises for Example 2

Name the longest side and the shortest side of the triangle.

4.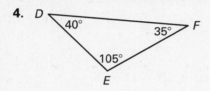

5.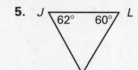

6.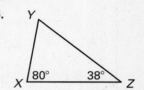

NAME_____ DATE _____

Reteaching with Practice

For use with pages 212–218

EXAMPLE 3 *Use the Triangle Inequality*

Can the side lengths form a triangle? Explain.

a. 7, 10, 15   **b.** 9, 11, 20   **c.** 12, 15, 30

SOLUTION

If the sum of the two shorter side lengths is greater than the longest side length, then they can form a triangle.

a. These side lengths are possible because $7 + 10 > 15$.

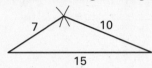

b. These side lengths are not possible because $9 + 11 = 20$.

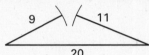

c. These side lengths are not possible because $12 + 15 < 30$.

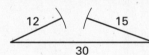

Exercises for Example 3

Can the side lengths form a triangle? Explain.

7. 14, 17, 31

8. 4, 7, 15

9. 9, 17, 23

Geometry, Concepts and Skills
Practice Workbook with Examples

Reteaching with Practice

For use with pages 233–239

GOAL **Identify congruent triangles and corresponding parts.**

VOCABULARY

When two triangles have exactly the same size and shape, the sides and angles that are the same in the triangles are called **corresponding parts.**

When all pairs of corresponding angles are congruent and all pairs of corresponding sides are congruent in two figures, the figures are **congruent.**

EXAMPLE 1 *Write a Congruence Statement*

The two triangles at the right are congruent.

a. Identify all corresponding congruent parts.

b. Write a congruence statement.

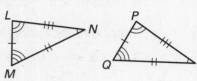

SOLUTION

a. **Corresponding Angles**   **Corresponding Sides**

$\angle M \cong \angle Q$ $\overline{LM} \cong \overline{PQ}$

$\angle L \cong \angle P$ $\overline{LN} \cong \overline{PR}$

$\angle N \cong \angle R$ $\overline{MN} \cong \overline{QR}$

b. List the letters of the triangle names so that the corresponding angles match. One possible congruence statement is $\triangle MLN \cong \triangle QPR$.

Exercises for Example 1

The triangles are congruent. Identify all pairs of corresponding congruent parts. Then write a congruence statement.

1.

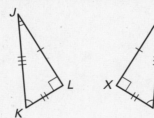

2.

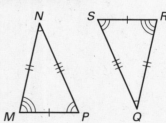

NAME_____ DATE _____

Reteaching with Practice

EXAMPLE 2 *Use Properties of Congruent Triangles*

In the figure, $\triangle ABC \cong \triangle KLM$.

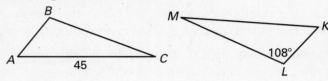

a. Find the length of $\overline{KM}$

b. Find $m\angle B$.

SOLUTION

a. Because $\overline{KM} \cong \overline{AC}$, you know that $KM = AC = 45$.

b. Because $\angle B \cong \angle L$, you know that $m\angle B = m\angle L = 108°$.

Exercises for Example 2

3. $\triangle ABC \cong \triangle DEF$. Find the length of $\overline{DE}$ and $m\angle C$.

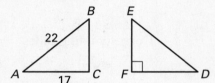

4. $\triangle ABC \cong \triangle DEF$. Find the length of $\overline{BC}$ and $m\angle F$.

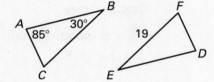

NAME _____ DATE _____

Reteaching with Practice

For use with pages 233–239

EXAMPLE 3 *Determine Whether Triangles are Congruent*

In the figure, $\overline{AB} \parallel \overline{CD}$ and $\overline{BC} \parallel \overline{AD}$. Determine whether the two triangles are congruent. If they are, write a congruence statement.

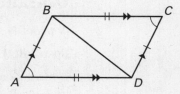

SOLUTION

Start with the information marked in the diagram, $\overline{AB} \cong \overline{CD}$, $\overline{BC} \cong \overline{DA}$, and $\angle A \cong \angle C$. Then label any information you can deduce from the figure.

$\overline{BD} \cong \overline{BD}$	Reflexive Property of Congruence
$\angle ABD \cong \angle CDB$	Alternate interior angles are congruent.
$\angle ADB \cong \angle CBD$	Alternate interior angles are congruent.

Since all corresponding parts are congruent, $\triangle ABD \cong \triangle CDB$.

Exercises for Example 3

Determine whether the triangles are congruent. If so, write a congruence statement.

5.

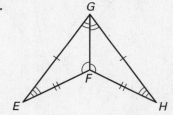

6.

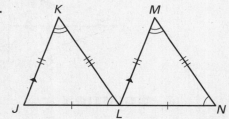

Geometry, Concepts and Skills
Practice Workbook with Examples

NAME _____ DATE _____

Reteaching with Practice

For use with pages 240–249

CALIFORNIA
Geometry Content Standards
5.0

GOAL Show triangles are congruent using SSS and SAS.

VOCABULARY

A **proof** is a convincing argument that shows why a statement is true.

Postulate 12   Side-Side-Side Congruence Postulate (SSS)

If three sides of one triangle are congruent to three sides of a second triangle, then the two triangles are congruent.

Postulate 13   Side-Angle-Side Congruence Postulate (SAS)

If two sides and the included angle of one triangle are congruent to two sides and the included angle of a second triangle, then the two triangles are congruent.

EXAMPLE 1 *Use the SSS Congruence Postulate*

Does the diagram give enough information to use the SSS Congruence Postulate? Explain your reasoning.

a.
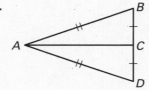

b.
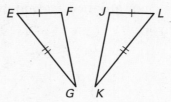

SOLUTION

a. From the diagram, you know that $\overline{BC} \cong \overline{DC}$ and $\overline{AB} \cong \overline{AD}$. By the Reflexive Property, you know that $\overline{AC} \cong \overline{AC}$. Because all three pairs of corresponding sides are congruent, you can use the SSS Congruence Postulate to conclude that $\triangle ABC \cong \triangle ADC$.

b. You know that $\overline{EF} \cong \overline{LJ}$ and $\overline{EG} \cong \overline{LK}$. There is not enough information provided to determine whether the corresponding third sides are congruent or not. So, you cannot use the SSS Congruence Postulate.

Reteaching with Practice

For use with pages 240–249

Exercises for Example 1

**Does the diagram give enough information to use the
SSS Congruence Postulate? Explain your reasoning.**

1.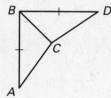

2.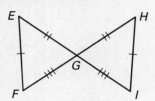

EXAMPLE 2 *Use the SAS Congruence Postulate*

Does the diagram give enough information to use the SAS Congruence
Postulate? Explain.

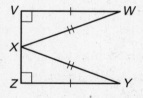

SOLUTION

From the diagram, you know that $\overline{VW} \cong \overline{YZ}$ and $\overline{WX} \cong \overline{XY}$. $\angle V \cong \angle Z$
because they are both right angles. But $\angle V$ is not the angle included by
$\overline{VW}$ and $\overline{WX}$, and $\angle Z$ is not the angle included by $\overline{YZ}$ and $\overline{XY}$. So, you
cannot use the SAS Congruence Postulate.

Reteaching with Practice

For use with pages 240–249

Exercises for Example 2

Does the diagram give enough information to use the SAS Congruence Postulate? Explain.

3.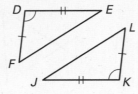

4.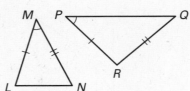

EXAMPLE 3 **Prove Triangles are Congruent**

Given that $\overline{AB} \cong \overline{ED}$, $\overline{AB} \parallel \overline{ED}$ and $\overline{AE}$ bisects $\overline{BD}$, write a proof to show that $\triangle ABC \cong \triangle EDC$.

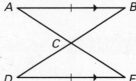

SOLUTION

Statements	Reasons
1. $\overline{AB} \cong \overline{ED}$	1. Given
2. $\overline{AB} \parallel \overline{ED}$	2. Given
3. $\overline{AE}$ bisects $\overline{BD}$.	3. Given
4. $\overline{BC} \cong \overline{DC}$	4. Definition of segment bisector
5. $\angle B \cong \angle D$	5. Alternate Interior Angles Theorem
6. $\triangle ABC \cong \triangle EDC$	6. SAS Congruence Postulate

Exercise for Example 3

Fill in the missing statements and reasons.

5. Given: $\overline{WZ} \cong \overline{YZ}$, $\overline{XZ}$ bisects $\angle WZY$.
Prove: $\triangle WXZ \cong \triangle YXZ$

Statements	Reasons
1. _____	1. Given
2. $\overline{XZ}$ bisects $\angle WZY$.	2. _____
3. _____	3. Definition of angle bisector
4. $\overline{XZ} \cong \overline{XZ}$	4. _____
5. $\triangle WXZ \cong \triangle YXZ$	5. _____

NAME _____ DATE _____

Reteaching with Practice

For use with pages 250–256

CALIFORNIA
Geometry Content Standards
5.0

GOAL Show triangles are congruent using ASA and AAS.

VOCABULARY

Postulate 14   Angle-Side-Angle Congruence Postulate (ASA)

If two angles and the included side of one triangle are congruent to two angles and the included side of a second triangle, then the two triangles are congruent.

Theorem 5.1   Angle-Angle-Side Congruence Theorem (AAS)

If two angles and a non-included side of one triangle are congruent to two angles and the corresponding non-included side of a second triangle, then the two triangles are congruent.

EXAMPLE 1 *Determine When to Use ASA Congruence*

Based on the diagram, can you use the ASA Congruence Postulate to show that the triangles are congruent? Explain your reasoning.

a. 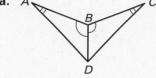   **b.**

SOLUTION

a. From the diagram, you know that ∠ABD ≅ ∠CBD and ∠A ≅ ∠C. By the Reflexive Property of Congruence, you know that $\overline{BD} \cong \overline{BD}$. But $\overline{BD}$ is not the side included by the congruent angles in either triangle, so you cannot use the ASA Congruence Postulate.

b. You know that $\overline{EF} \cong \overline{JL}$, ∠F ≅ ∠L, and ∠E ≅ ∠J. $\overline{EF}$ is the side included by ∠F and ∠E, and $\overline{JL}$ is the side included by ∠L and ∠J. So, you can use the ASA Congruence Postulate to conclude that △EFG ≅ △JLK. Notice that the given information $\overline{FG} \cong \overline{LK}$ is not needed.

NAME _____ DATE _____

Reteaching with Practice

For use with pages 250–256

Exercises for Example 1

Does the diagram give enough information to use the ASA Congruence Postulate? Explain.

1.

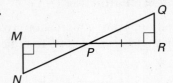

2.

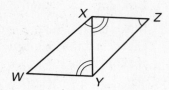

EXAMPLE 2 *Determine When to Use AAS Congruence*

Based on the diagram, can you use the AAS Congruence Theorem to show that the triangles are congruent? If not, what additional congruence is needed?

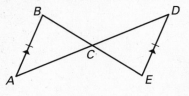

SOLUTION

You are given $\overline{AB} \cong \overline{DE}$. $\angle A \cong \angle D$ since they are alternate interior angles and $\overline{AB} \parallel \overline{DE}$. $\angle ACB \cong \angle DCE$ since they are vertical angles. $\angle A$ and $\angle ACB$ make $\overline{AB}$ the non-included side, and $\angle D$ and $\angle DCE$ make $\overline{DE}$ the non-included side. So, you can use the AAS Congruence Theorem to show that $\triangle ABC \cong \triangle DEC$.

Exercises for Example 2

Based on the diagram, can you use the AAS Congruence Theorem to show that the triangles are congruent? If not, what additional congruence is needed?

3.

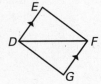

4.

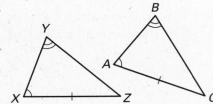

Reteaching with Practice

For use with pages 250–256

EXAMPLE 3 *Decide Whether Triangles are Congruent*

Does the diagram give enough information to show that the
triangles are congruent? If so, state the postulate or theorem
you would use.

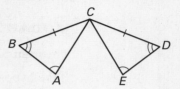

SOLUTION

$\angle A \cong \angle E$ Given

$\angle B \cong \angle D$ Given

$\overline{BC} \cong \overline{DC}$ Given

Use the AAS Congruence Theorem to conclude that $\triangle ABC \cong \triangle EDC$.

Exercises for Example 3

**Does the diagram give enough information to show that the triangles
are congruent? If so, state the postulate or theorem you would use.**

5.

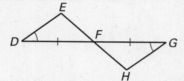

6.

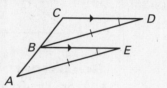

7. $\overline{KL}$ bisects $\overline{JM}$

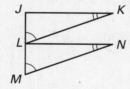

NAME_____ DATE _____

Reteaching with Practice

For use with pages 257–264

CALIFORNIA
Geometry Content Standards
5.0

GOAL Use the HL Congruence Theorem and summarize congruence postulates and theorems.

VOCABULARY

Theorem 5.2   Hypotenuse-Leg Congruence Theorem (HL)

If the hypotenuse and a leg of a right triangle are congruent to the hypotenuse and a leg of a second right triangle, then the two triangles are congruent.

EXAMPLE 1 *Determine When to Use HL*

Does the diagram give enough information to show that the triangles are congruent? Explain.

a.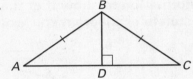

b.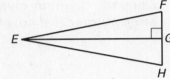

SOLUTION

a. From the diagram, you know that $\triangle ABD$ and $\triangle CBD$ are right triangles. By the Reflexive Property, you know $\overline{BD} \cong \overline{BD}$ (leg) and you are given that $\overline{AB} \cong \overline{CB}$ (hypotenuse). You can use the HL Congruence Theorem to show that $\triangle ABD \cong \triangle CBD$.

b. You know that $\triangle EFG$ and $\triangle EHG$ are right triangles. By the Reflexive Property, you know that $\overline{EG} \cong \overline{EG}$ (leg). But you also need to know that $\overline{EF} \cong \overline{EH}$ (hypotenuse). This information is not provided, so you cannot use the HL Congruence Theorem.

Exercises for Example 1

Does the diagram give enough information to use the HL Congruence Theorem? Explain.

1.

2. $\overline{QS}$ bisects $\overline{RT}$.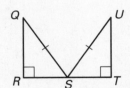

Geometry, Concepts and Skills
Practice Workbook with Examples

NAME_____ DATE _____

Reteaching with Practice

For use with pages 257–264

EXAMPLE 2 **Decide Whether Triangles are Congruent**

Does the diagram give enough information to prove that the triangles are congruent? If so, state the postulate or theorem you would use.

a.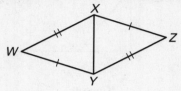

b.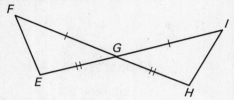

SOLUTION

a. From the diagram, you know that $\overline{WY} \cong \overline{ZX}$ and $\overline{WX} \cong \overline{ZY}$. By the Reflexive Property, you know that $\overline{XY} \cong \overline{XY}$. You can use the SSS Congruence Postulate to prove that $\triangle WYX \cong \triangle ZXY$.

b. You know that $\overline{FG} \cong \overline{IG}$ and $\overline{EG} \cong \overline{HG}$. $\angle EGF$ and $\angle HGI$ are vertical angles, so $\angle EGF \cong \angle HGI$. $\angle EGF$ is the angle included by sides $\overline{FG}$ and $\overline{EG}$ in $\triangle EFG$. $\angle HGI$ is the angle included by sides $\overline{IG}$ and $\overline{HG}$ in $\triangle HIG$. You can use the SAS Congruence Postulate to prove that $\triangle EFG \cong \triangle HIG$.

Exercises for Example 2

Does the diagram give enough information to prove that the triangles are congruent? If so, state the postulate or theorem you would use.

3.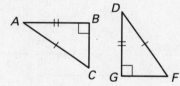

4.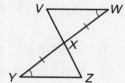

5.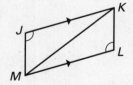

NAME _____ DATE _____

Reteaching with Practice

For use with pages 257–264

EXAMPLE 3 *Prove Triangles are Congruent*

Prove that $\triangle ABC \cong \triangle ECD$.

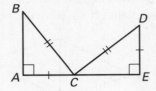

SOLUTION

Statements	Reasons
1. $\triangle ABC$ and $\triangle ECD$ are right triangles.	1. Given
2. $\overline{AC} \cong \overline{ED}$, $\overline{BC} \cong \overline{CD}$	2. Given
3. $\triangle ABC \cong \triangle ECD$	3. HL Congruence Theorem

Exercise for Example 3

Fill in the missing statements and reasons.

6. Given: $\angle R \cong \angle U$, $\overline{ST}$ bisects $\angle RSU$.
   Prove: $\triangle RST \cong \triangle UST$

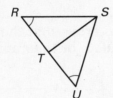

Statements	Reasons
1. $\overline{ST}$ bisects $\angle RSU$.	1. _____
2. _____	2. Definition of Angle Bisector
3. $\angle R \cong \angle U$	3. _____
4. _____	4. Reflexive Property of Congruence
5. $\triangle RST \cong \triangle UST$	5. _____

NAME _____ DATE _____

Reteaching with Practice

For use with pages 265–271

CALIFORNIA
Geometry Content Standards

5.0

GOAL Show corresponding parts of congruent triangles are congruent.

EXAMPLE 1 *Show Corresponding Parts are Congruent*

Given: $\overline{CD}$ bisects $\overline{BE}$, $\overline{AE} \cong \overline{BC}$, $\overline{AB} \cong \overline{CD}$

Prove: $\overline{BE} \cong \overline{DE}$

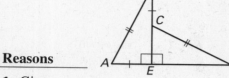

SOLUTION

Statements	Reasons
1. $\overline{AE} \cong \overline{BC}$, $\overline{CD}$ bisects $\overline{BE}$.	1. Given
2. $\overline{BC} \cong \overline{CE}$	2. Definition of segment bisector
3. $\overline{AE} \cong \overline{CE}$	3. Transitive Property of Congruence
4. $\overline{AB} \cong \overline{CD}$	4. Given
5. $\triangle AEB$ and $\triangle CED$ are right triangles.	5. Definition of right triangles
6. $\triangle AEB \cong \triangle CED$	6. HL Congruence Theorem
7. $\overline{BE} \cong \overline{DE}$	7. Corresponding parts of congruent triangles are congruent.

Exercises for Example 1

Fill in the missing statements and reasons.

1. Given: $\overline{GK}$ bisects $\overline{FH}$, $\overline{FJ} \parallel \overline{GK}$, $\overline{JG} \parallel \overline{KH}$

   Prove: $\angle J \cong \angle K$

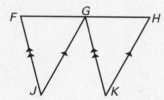

Statements	Reasons
1. $\overline{GK}$ bisects $\overline{FH}$.	1. _____
2. $\overline{FG} \cong \overline{GH}$	2. _____
3. _____	3. Given
4. $\angle F \cong \angle HGK$, $\angle FGJ \cong \angle H$	4. _____
5. _____	5. ASA Congruence Postulate
6. _____	6. Corresponding parts of congruent triangles are congruent.

Reteaching with Practice

For use with pages 265–271

2. Given: $\overline{AC}$ bisects $\angle BAD$, $\angle B \cong \angle D$
   Prove: $\overline{BC} \cong \overline{DC}$

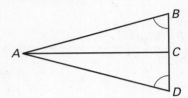

Statements	Reasons
1. $\overline{AC}$ bisects $\angle BAD$.	**1.** _____
2. _____	**2.** Definition of angle bisector
3. _____	**3.** Given
4. $\overline{AC} \cong \overline{AC}$	**4.** _____
5. $\triangle ACB \cong \triangle ACD$	**5.** _____
6. $\overline{BC} \cong \overline{DC}$	**6.** _____

EXAMPLE 2 *Use Overlapping Triangles*

Redraw the triangle separately and label all congruences.
Then show $\overline{RP} \cong \overline{TQ}$, given $\angle R \cong \angle T$ and $\angle RQP \cong \angle TPQ$.

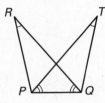

SOLUTION

1. Sketch the triangles separately. Then label the given
   information and any other information you can
   deduce from the diagram.

   In the original diagram, $\overline{PQ}$ is the same in both
   triangles ($\overline{PQ} \cong \overline{QP}$).

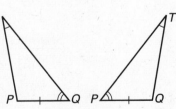

2. Show $\triangle PQR \cong \triangle QPT$ to prove $\overline{RP} \cong \overline{TQ}$.

Statements	Reasons
1. $\angle R \cong \angle T$	**1.** Given
2. $\angle RQP \cong \angle TPQ$	**2.** Given
3. $\overline{PQ} \cong \overline{PQ}$	**3.** Reflexive Property of Congruence
4. $\triangle PQR \cong \triangle QPT$	**4.** AAS Congruence Theorem
5. $\overline{RP} \cong \overline{TQ}$	**5.** Corresponding parts of congruent triangles are congruent.

Geometry, Concepts and Skills
Practice Workbook with Examples

NAME _____ DATE _____

Reteaching with Practice

For use with pages 265–271

Exercises for Example 2

Redraw the triangles separately and label all congruences.
Then fill in the missing statements and reasons to show that
the triangles or corresponding parts are congruent.

3. Given: $\overline{MN} \cong \overline{ML}$, $\overline{JM} \cong \overline{KM}$
   Prove: $\triangle JLM \cong \triangle KNM$

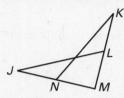

Statements	Reasons
1. $\overline{MN} \cong \overline{ML}$	1. _____
2. _____	2. Given
3. _____	3. Reflexive Property of Congruence
4. $\triangle JLM \cong \triangle KNM$	4. _____

4. Given: $\overline{WY} \cong \overline{XZ}$, $\overline{WZ} \cong \overline{XY}$
   Prove: $\angle Z \cong \angle Y$

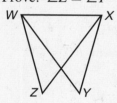

Statements	Reasons
1. _____	1. Given
2. $\overline{WZ} \cong \overline{XY}$	2. _____
3. $\overline{WX} \cong \overline{WX}$	3. _____
4. _____	4. SSS Congruence Postulate
5. $\angle Z \cong \angle Y$	5. _____

Geometry, Concepts and Skills
Practice Workbook with Examples

NAME_____ DATE_____

Reteaching with Practice

For use with pages 272–280

CALIFORNIA
Geometry Content Standards
16.0

GOAL Use angle bisectors and perpendicular bisectors.

VOCABULARY

The **distance from a point to a line** is measured by the length of the perpendicular segment from the point to the line.

When a point is the same distance from one line as it is from another line, the point is **equidistant** from the two lines.

A segment, ray, or line that is perpendicular to a segment at its midpoint is called a **perpendicular bisector.**

Theorem 5.3   Angle Bisector Theorem

If a point is on the bisector of an angle, then it is equidistant from the two sides of the angle.

Theorem 5.4   Perpendicular Bisector Theorem

If a point is on the perpendicular bisector of a segment, then it is equidistant from the endpoints of the segment.

EXAMPLE 1 *Use Angle Bisectors*

Use the diagram to find the value of the variable.

a. 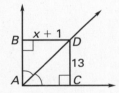   b.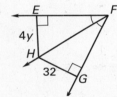

SOLUTION

a. In the diagram, $\overrightarrow{AD}$ is the angle bisector of $\angle BAC$.

$x + 1 = 13$ By the Angle Bisector Theorem, $BD = CD$.

$x = 12$ Subtract 1 from each side.

b. In the diagram, $\overrightarrow{FH}$ is the angle bisector of $\angle EFG$.

$4y = 32$ By the Angle Bisector Theorem, $EH = GH$.

$y = 8$ Divide each side by 4.

NAME_____ DATE _____

Reteaching with Practice

For use with pages 272–280

Exercises for Example 1

Find the value of *x*.

1.

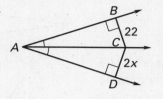

2.

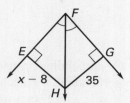

3.

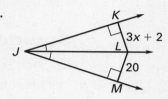

EXAMPLE 2 *Use Perpendicular Bisectors*

Use the diagram to find the value of the variable.

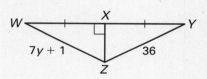

SOLUTION

In the diagram, $\overline{XZ}$ is the perpendicular bisector of $\overline{WY}$.

$7y + 1 = 36$	By the Perpendicular Bisector Theorem, $WZ = YZ$.
$7y = 35$	Subtract 1 from each side.
$y = 5$	Divide each side by 7.

Exercises for Example 2

Find the value of *x*.

4.

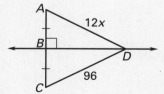

5.

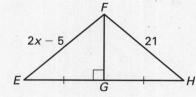

6.

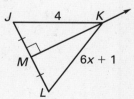

Reteaching with Practice

For use with pages 272–280

EXAMPLE 3 *Use Intersecting Bisectors of a Triangle*

Find the value of x.

SOLUTION

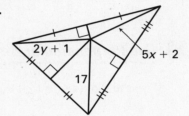

$\overline{BG}$, $\overline{DG}$, and $\overline{FG}$ are perpendicular bisectors of $\triangle ACE$.
You know that the perpendicular bisectors of a triangle
intersect at a point that is equidistant from the vertices of
the triangle. So, $CG = EG$.

$x - 4 = 15$ Substitute $x - 4$ for CG and 15 for EG.

$x = 19$ Add 4 to each side.

Exercises for Example 3

Find the value of x. Then find the value of y.

7.

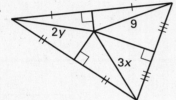

8.

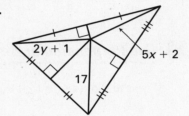

NAME_____ DATE _____

Reteaching with Practice

For use with pages 281–290

CALIFORNIA
Geometry Content Standards
22.0

GOAL Identify and use reflections and lines of symmetry.

VOCABULARY

A **reflection** is a transformation that creates a mirror image.

A figure in the plane has a **line of symmetry** if the figure can be reflected onto itself by a reflection in the line.

Properties of Reflections

A reflection has all three of these properties:

1. The reflected image is congruent to the original figure.

2. The orientation of the reflected image is reversed.

3. The line of reflection is the perpendicular bisector of the segments joining the corresponding points.

EXAMPLE 1 *Identify Reflections*

Tell whether the black figure is a reflection of the white figure in line ℓ.

a.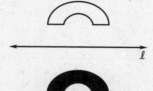

b.

SOLUTION

Check to see if all three properties of a reflection are met.

a. Yes.   **1.** Is the image congruent to the original figure?   b. Yes.

  No.   **2.** Is the orientation of the image reversed?   Yes.

  No.   **3.** Is ℓ the perpendicular bisector of the segments connecting the corresponding points?   To check, draw a diagram and connect the corresponding parts. Yes.

Answer:

a. Because two of the properties were not met, the black figure is not a reflection of the white figure.

b. Because all three properties are met, the black triangle is a reflection of the white triangle in line ℓ.

NAME_____ DATE _____

Reteaching with Practice

For use with pages 281–290

Exercise for Example 1

1. Tell whether the black figure is a reflection of the white figure in line ℓ.

EXAMPLE 2 *Reflections in a Coordinate Plane*

Tell whether $\triangle DEF$ is a reflection of $\triangle ABC$. If $\triangle DEF$ is a reflection, name the line of reflection.

a.
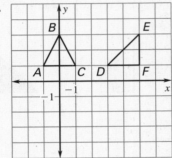

b.
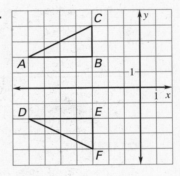

SOLUTION

a. $\triangle DEF$ is not a reflection of $\triangle ABC$ because the triangles are not congruent.

b. $\triangle DEF$ is a reflection of $\triangle ABC$ because the triangles are congruent, the orientation of $\triangle ABC$ is reversed, and the x-axis is the perpendicular bisector of $\overline{AD}$, $\overline{BE}$, and all segments joining corresponding points. The x-axis is the line of reflection.

Exercise for Example 2

2. Tell whether $\triangle DEF$ is a reflection of $\triangle ABC$. If $\triangle DEF$ is a reflection, name the line of reflection.

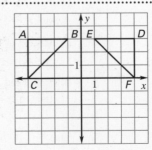

Geometry, Concepts and Skills
Practice Workbook with Examples

NAME _____ DATE _____

Reteaching with Practice

For use with pages 281–290

EXAMPLE 3 **Determine Lines of Symmetry**

Determine the number of lines of symmetry in the figure.

SOLUTION

Think about how many different ways you can fold the figure so that the edges of the figure match up perfectly. There are 5 lines of symmetry.

Exercises for Example 3

Determine the number of lines of symmetry in the figure.

3.

4.

5.

NAME_____ DATE _____

Reteaching with Practice

For use with pages 303–308

CALIFORNIA
Geometry Content Standards
12.0

GOAL Identify and classify polygons. Find angle measures of quadrilaterals.

VOCABULARY

A **polygon** is a plane figure that is formed by three or more segments called **sides**. The endpoint of each side is a **vertex**.

A segment that joins two nonconsecutive vertices of a polygon is called a **diagonal**.

Polygons are classified by the number of sides they have. A **triangle** has three sides. A **quadrilateral** has four sides. A **pentagon** has five sides. A **hexagon** has six sides. A **heptagon** has seven sides. An **octagon** has eight sides.

Theorem 6.1   Quadrilateral Interior Angles Theorem
The sum of the measures of the interior angles of a quadrilateral is 360°.

EXAMPLE 1   *Identify Polygons*

Tell whether the figure is a polygon. Explain your reasoning.

a. 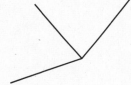   b. 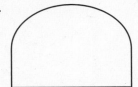   c.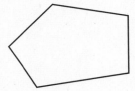

SOLUTION

a. No, the figure is not a polygon because each side intersects two other sides at one vertex, and no other sides at the other vertex.

b. No, the figure is not a polygon because it has a side that is not a segment.

c. Yes, the figure is a polygon formed by five straight sides.

Exercises for Example 1

Tell whether the figure is a polygon. Explain your reasoning.

1. 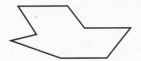   2.    3.

NAME_____ DATE _____

Reteaching with Practice

For use with pages 303–308

4.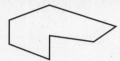

5.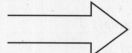

EXAMPLE 2 *Classify Polygons*

Decide whether the figure is a polygon. If so, tell what type. If not, explain why.

a.    **b.**    **c.**

SOLUTION

a. The figure is a polygon with seven sides, so it is a heptagon.

b. The figure is not a polygon because two of the sides intersect only one other side.

c. The figure is a polygon with six sides, so it is a hexagon.

Exercises for Example 2

Decide whether the figure is a polygon. If so, tell what type. If not, explain why.

6.    **7.**

8.

Geometry, Concepts and Skills
Practice Workbook with Examples

NAME _____ DATE _____

Reteaching with Practice

For use with pages 303–308

EXAMPLE 3 *Use the Quadrilateral Interior Angles Theorem*

Find the value of x.

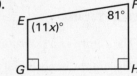

SOLUTION

Use the fact that the sum of the measures of the interior
angles of a quadrilateral is 360°.

$m\angle A + m\angle B + m\angle C + m\angle D = 360°$	Quadrilateral Interior Angles Theorem
$50° + 118° + 84° + 2x° = 360°$	Substitute angle measures.
$252 + 2x = 360$	Simplify.
$2x = 108$	Subtract 252 from each side.
$x = 54$	Divide each side by 2.

Exercises for Example 3

Find the value of *x*.

9.

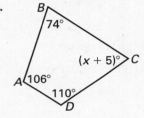

10.

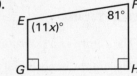

11.

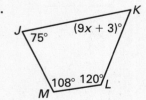

Geometry, Concepts and Skills
Practice Workbook with Examples

Reteaching with Practice

For use with pages 309–315

CALIFORNIA
Geometry Content Standards
7.0

GOAL Use properties of parallelograms.

VOCABULARY

A **parallelogram** is a quadrilateral with both pairs of opposite sides parallel.

Theorem 6.2
If a quadrilateral is a parallelogram, then its opposite sides are congruent.

Theorem 6.3
If a quadrilateral is a parallelogram, then its opposite angles are congruent.

Theorem 6.4
If a quadrilateral is a parallelogram, then its consecutive angles are supplementary.

Theorem 6.5
If a quadrilateral is a parallelogram, then its diagonals bisect each other.

EXAMPLE 1 *Find Side Lengths of Parallelograms*

$ABCD$ is a parallelogram. Find the values of x and y.

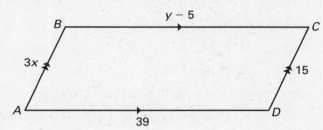

SOLUTION

$AB = CD$	Opposite sides of a parallelogram are congruent.
$3x = 15$	Substitute $3x$ for AB and 15 for CD.
$x = 5$	Divide each side by 3.
$BC = AD$	Opposite sides of a parallelogram are congruent.
$y - 5 = 39$	Substitute $y - 5$ for BC and 39 for AD.
$y = 44$	Add 5 to each side.

NAME_____ DATE _____

Reteaching with Practice

For use with pages 309–315

Exercises for Example 1

Find the values of *x* and *y* in the parallelogram.

1.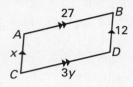

2.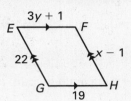

3.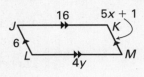

EXAMPLE 2 *Find Angle Measures of Parallelograms*

ABDC is a parallelogram. Find the values of *x* and *y*.

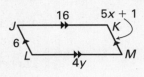

SOLUTION

By Theorem 6.4, the consecutive angles of a parallelogram
are supplementary.

$m\angle A + m\angle C = 180°$	Theorem 6.4
$72° + x° = 180°$	Substitute 72° for $m\angle A$ and $x°$ for $m\angle C$.
$x = 108$	Subtract 72 from each side.

By Theorem 6.3, the opposite angles of a parallelogram are congruent.

$m\angle A = m\angle D$	Opposite angles of a ▱ are congruent.
$72° = 3y°$	Substitute 72° for $m\angle A$ and $3y°$ for $m\angle D$.
$24 = y$	Divide each side by 3.

Exercises for Example 2

Find the values of *x* and *y* in the parallelogram.

4.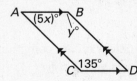

5.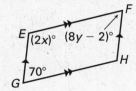

6.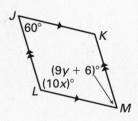

Geometry, Concepts and Skills
Practice Workbook with Examples

Reteaching with Practice

For use with pages 309–315

EXAMPLE 3 **Find Segment Lengths**

ABCD is a parallelogram. Find the values of *x* and *y*.

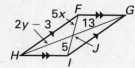

SOLUTION

By Theorem 6.5, the diagonals bisect each other.

BE = *DE*	Diagonals of a ▱ bisect each other.
6 = *x*	Substitute 6 for *BE* and *x* for *DE*.

Use Theorem 6.5 again for the other diagonal.

AE = *CE*	Diagonals of a ▱ bisect each other.
9 = 3*y*	Substitute 9 for *AE* and 3*y* for *CE*.
3 = *y*	Divide each side by 3.

Exercises for Example 3

Find the values of *x* and *y* in the parallelogram.

7.

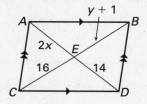

8.

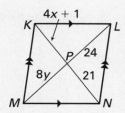

9.

NAME_____ DATE _____

Reteaching with Practice

For use with pages 316–324

CALIFORNIA
Geometry Content Standards
7.0

GOAL Show that a quadrilateral is a parallelogram.

VOCABULARY

Theorem 6.6
If both pairs of opposite sides of a quadrilateral are congruent, then the quadrilateral is a parallelogram.

Theorem 6.7
If both pairs of opposite angles of a quadrilateral are congruent, then the quadrilateral is a parallelogram.

Theorem 6.8
If an angle of a quadrilateral is supplementary to both of its consecutive angles, then the quadrilateral is a parallelogram.

Theorem 6.9
If the diagonals of a quadrilateral bisect each other, then the quadrilateral is a parallelogram.

EXAMPLE 1 *Use Opposite Sides*

Tell whether the quadrilateral is a parallelogram. Explain your reasoning.

a.

b.

SOLUTION

a. The quadrilateral is a parallelogram because both pairs of opposite sides are congruent.

b. The quadrilateral is not a parallelogram. Both pairs of opposite sides are not congruent.

NAME _____ DATE _____

Reteaching with Practice

For use with pages 316–324

Exercises for Example 1

Tell whether the quadrilateral is a parallelogram. Explain your reasoning.

1. 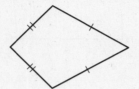   2. 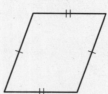   3.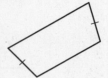

EXAMPLE 2 ## Use Opposite Angles

Tell whether the quadrilateral is a parallelogram. Explain your reasoning.

a. 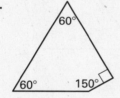   b.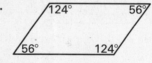

SOLUTION

a. The quadrilateral is not a parallelogram. Both pairs of opposite angles are not congruent.

b. The quadrilateral is a parallelogram because both pairs of opposite angles are congruent.

Exercises for Example 2

Tell whether the quadrilateral is a parallelogram. Explain your reasoning.

4. 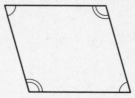   5. 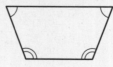   6.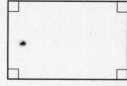

NAME _____ DATE _____

Reteaching with Practice

For use with pages 316–324

EXAMPLE 3 **Use Diagonals and Consecutive Angles**

Tell whether the quadrilateral is a parallelogram. Explain your reasoning.

a.

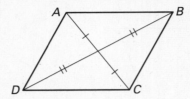

b.

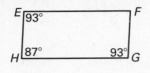

SOLUTION

a. The diagonals of *ABCD* bisect each other. So, by Theorem 6.9, *ABCD* is a parallelogram.

b. $\angle H$ is supplementary to $\angle E$ and $\angle G$ ($87° + 93° = 180°$). So, by Theorem 6.8, *EFGH* is a parallelogram.

Exercises for Example 3

Tell whether the quadrilateral is a parallelogram. Explain your reasoning.

7.

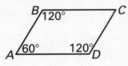

8.

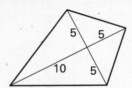

9.

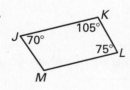

Geometry, Concepts and Skills
Practice Workbook with Examples

Reteaching with Practice

For use with pages 325–330

CALIFORNIA
Geometry Content Standards
7.0

GOAL Use properties of special types of parallelograms.

VOCABULARY

A **rhombus** is a parallelogram with four congruent sides.

A **rectangle** is a parallelogram with four right angles.

A **square** is a parallelogram with four congruent sides and four right angles.

Rhombus Corollary
If a quadrilateral has four congruent sides, then it is a rhombus.

Rectangle Corollary
If a quadrilateral has four right angles, then it is a rectangle.

Square Corollary
If a quadrilateral has four congruent sides and four right angles, then it is a square.

Theorem 6.10
The diagonals of a rhombus are perpendicular.

Theorem 6.11
The diagonals of a rectangle are congruent.

EXAMPLE 1 *Use Properties of Special Parallelograms*

In the diagram, *ABCD* is a square.

Find the values of *x* and *y*.

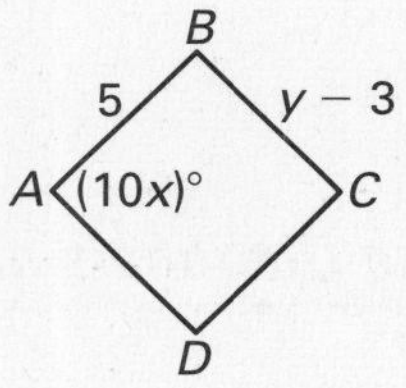

SOLUTION

By definition, a square has four right angles.

$$m\angle A = 90° \qquad \text{Definition of a square}$$

$$10x° = 90° \qquad \text{Substitute } 10x° \text{ for } m\angle A.$$

$$x = 9 \qquad \text{Divide each side by 10.}$$

By definition, a square has four congruent sides. So, $AB = BC$.

$$5 = y - 3 \qquad \text{Substitute 5 for } AB \text{ and } y - 3 \text{ for } BC.$$

$$8 = y \qquad \text{Add 3 to each side.}$$

Reteaching with Practice

For use with pages 325–330

Exercises for Example 1

Find the values of the variables.

1. rectangle *ABCD*

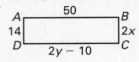

2. rhombus *EFGH*

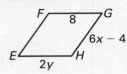

3. square *JKLM*

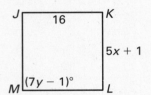

EXAMPLE 2 *Use Diagonals of a Rhombus*

JKLM is a rhombus.
Find the value of *x*.

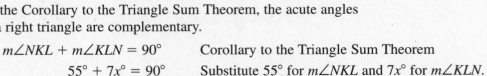

SOLUTION

By Theorem 6.10, the diagonals of a rhombus are perpendicular.
Therefore, ∠*KNL* is a right angle, so △ *KNL* is a right triangle.

By the Corollary to the Triangle Sum Theorem, the acute angles
of a right triangle are complementary.

$m\angle NKL + m\angle KLN = 90°$	Corollary to the Triangle Sum Theorem
$55° + 7x° = 90°$	Substitute 55° for $m\angle NKL$ and $7x°$ for $m\angle KLN$.
$7x = 35$	Subtract 55 from each side.
$x = 5$	Divide each side by 7.

Geometry, Concepts and Skills
Practice Workbook with Examples

NAME _____ DATE _____

Reteaching with Practice

For use with pages 325–330

Exercises for Example 2

Find the value of x.

4. rhombus *ABCD*

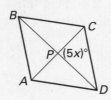

5. rhombus *EFGH*

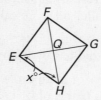

EXAMPLE 3 **Use Diagonals of a Rectangle**

ABCD is a rectangle. *AC* = 16.
BD = 5*x* + 1. Find the value of *x*.

SOLUTION

By Theorem 6.11, the diagonals of a rectangle are congruent.
Therefore, *AC* = *BD*.

16 = 5*x* + 1	Substitute 16 for *AC* and 5*x* + 1 for *BD*.
15 = 5*x*	Subtract 1 from each side.
3 = *x*	Divide each side by 5.

Exercises for Example 3

Find the value of x.

6. rectangle *EFGH*, *EG* = 48, *HF* = 6*x*

7. rectangle *WXYZ*, *XZ* = 37, *WY* = 5*x* + 2

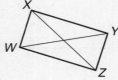

NAME_____ DATE _____

Reteaching with Practice

For use with pages 331–336

CALIFORNIA
Geometry Content Standards
7.0

GOAL Use properties of trapezoids.

VOCABULARY

A **trapezoid** is a quadrilateral with exactly one pair of parallel sides. The parallel sides are called the **bases**. The nonparallel sides are called the **legs**.

A trapezoid has two pairs of **base angles**.

If the legs of a trapezoid are congruent, then the trapezoid is an **isosceles trapezoid**.

The **midsegment of a trapezoid** is the segment that connects the midpoints of its legs.

Theorem 6.12
If a trapezoid is isosceles, then each pair of base angles is congruent.

Theorem 6.13
If a trapezoid has a pair of congruent base angles, then it is isosceles.

EXAMPLE 1 *Find Angle Measures of Trapezoids*

ABCD is a trapezoid.
Find the missing angle measures.

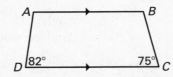

SOLUTION

By definition, a trapezoid has exactly one pair of parallel sides. In trapezoid *ABCD*, $\overline{AB} \parallel \overline{CD}$. Because $\angle A$ and $\angle D$ are same-side interior angles formed by parallel lines, they are supplementary. So, $m\angle A = 180° - m\angle D = 180° - 82° = 98°$.

Because $\angle B$ and $\angle C$ are same-side interior angles formed by parallel lines, they are supplementary. So, $m\angle B = 180° - m\angle C = 180° - 75° = 105°$.

Exercises for Example 1

EFGH is a trapezoid. Find the missing angle measures.

1.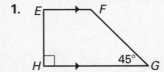

2.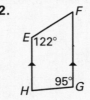

3.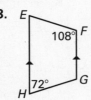

Reteaching with Practice

For use with pages 331–336

EXAMPLE 2 *Using Theorem 6.12*

ABCD is an isosceles trapezoid. Find the values of *x* and *y*.

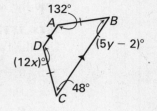

SOLUTION

By Theorem 6.12, each pair of base angles in an isosceles trapezoid is congruent. In trapezoid *ABCD*, $\angle A$ and $\angle D$ are a pair of base angles, and $\angle B$ and $\angle C$ are a pair of base angles.

$m\angle A = m\angle D$	Theorem 6.12
$132° = 12x°$	Substitute 132° for $m\angle A$ and $12x°$ for $m\angle D$.
$11 = x$	Divide each side by 12.
$m\angle B = m\angle C$	Theorem 6.12
$(5y - 2)° = 48°$	Substitute $(5y - 2)°$ for $m\angle B$ and 48° for $m\angle C$.
$5y = 50$	Add 2 to each side.
$y = 10$	Divide each side by 5.

Exercises for Example 2

Find the values of the variables.

4. isosceles trapezoid *EFGH*

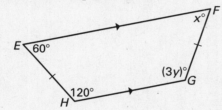

5. isosceles trapezoid *JKLM*

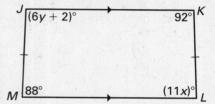

Reteaching with Practice

For use with pages 331–336

EXAMPLE 3 *Midsegment of a Trapezoid*

Find the length of the midsegment $\overline{AB}$ of trapezoid *JKLM*.

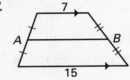

SOLUTION

Use the formula for the midsegment of a trapezoid.

$AB = \frac{1}{2}(JK + LM)$	Formula for midsegment of a trapezoid
$AB = \frac{1}{2}(17 + 13)$	Substitute 17 for *JK* and 13 for *LM*.
$AB = 15$	Simplify.

Exercises for Example 3

Find the length of the midsegment $\overline{AB}$ of the trapezoid.

6.

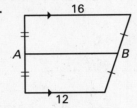

7.

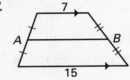

8.

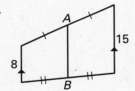

Geometry, Concepts and Skills
Practice Workbook with Examples

NAME _____ DATE _____

Reteaching with Practice

For use with pages 337–341

CALIFORNIA
Geometry Content Standards
7.0

GOAL Identify special quadrilaterals based on limited information.

EXAMPLE 1 *Use Properties of Quadrilaterals*

Determine whether the quadrilateral is a trapezoid, isosceles trapezoid, parallelogram, rectangle, rhombus, or square.

a.

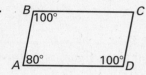

b.

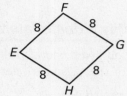

SOLUTION

a. The diagram shows that $\angle A$ is supplementary to $\angle B$ and to $\angle D$. Since one angle of the quadrilateral is supplementary to both of its consecutive angles, you know that *ABCD* is a parallelogram by Theorem 6.8.

b. The diagram shows that all four sides of quadrilateral *EFGH* have length 8. Since all four sides are congruent, *EFGH* is a rhombus.

Exercises for Example 1

Determine whether the quadrilateral is a trapezoid, isosceles trapezoid, parallelogram, rectangle, rhombus, or square.

1.

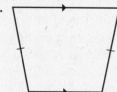

2.

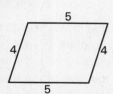

3.

4.

NAME_____ DATE _____

Reteaching with Practice

For use with pages 337–341

5.

6.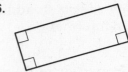

EXAMPLE 2 *Identify a Quadrilateral*

Are you given enough information to conclude that the figure is the given type of special quadrilateral? Explain your reasoning.

a. A rectangle?

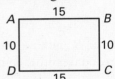

b. A square?

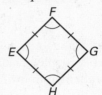

c. A parallelogram?

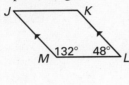

SOLUTION

a. The diagram shows that both pairs of opposite sides are congruent. Therefore, you know that *ABCD* is a parallelogram. For *ABCD* to be a rectangle, all four angles must be right angles. The diagram does not give any information about the angle measures, so you cannot conclude that *ABCD* is a rectangle.

b. The diagram shows that all four sides are congruent. Therefore, you know that *EFGH* is a rhombus. For *EFGH* to be a square, all four sides must be congruent and all four angles must be right angles. By the Quadrilateral Interior Angles Theorem, you know that the sum of the measures of the four angles must equal 360°. From the diagram, you know that all four angles have the same measure.

$$m\angle\ E + m\angle\ F + m\angle\ G + m\angle\ H = 360°$$ Quadrilateral Interior Angles Theorem

$$x° + x° + x° + x° = 360°$$ Substitute $x°$ for each angle measure.

$$4x = 360$$ Simplify.

$$x = 90$$ Divide each side by 4.

Because all four angles are right angles and all four sides are congruent, you know that *EFGH* is a square.

c. The diagram shows that one pair of opposite sides is parallel and the one pair of consecutive angles is supplementary (132° + 48° = 180°). There no information given about the second pair of opposite sides, nor is there any information given about any other pair of consecutive angles. Therefore, you cannot conclude that *JKLM* is a parallelogram.

Geometry, Concepts and Skills
Practice Workbook with Examples

NAME _____ DATE _____

Reteaching with Practice

For use with pages 337–341

Exercises for Example 2

Are you given enough information to conclude that the figure is the given type of special quadrilateral? Explain your reasoning.

7. An isosceles trapezoid?

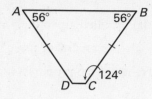

8. A rhombus?

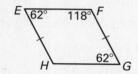

9. A parallelogram?

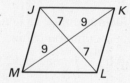

NAME_____ DATE _____

Reteaching with Practice

For use with pages 357–363

CALIFORNIA
Geometry Content Standards
1.0

GOAL Use ratios and proportions.

VOCABULARY

A **ratio** is a comparison of a number a and a nonzero number b using division.

An equation that states that two ratios are equal is called a **proportion**. In the proportion $\frac{a}{b} = \frac{c}{d}$, the numbers b and c are the **means** of the proportion. The numbers a and d are the **extremes** of the proportion.

Cross Product Property
In a proportion, the product of the extremes is equal to the product of the means.

EXAMPLE 1 *Simplify Ratios*

Simplify the ratio.

a. 6 days:15 days **b.** $\frac{2 \text{ ft}}{2 \text{ yd}}$

SOLUTION

a. 6 days:15 days can be written as the fraction $\frac{6 \text{ days}}{15 \text{ days}}$.

$$\frac{6 \text{ days}}{15 \text{ days}} = \frac{6 \div 3}{15 \div 3}$$
Divide numerator and denominator by their greatest common factor, 3.

$$= \frac{2}{5}$$
Simplify. $\frac{2}{5}$ is read as "2 to 5."

b. $\frac{2 \text{ ft}}{2 \text{ yd}} = \frac{2 \text{ ft}}{2 \cdot 3 \text{ ft}}$
Substitute 3 ft for 1 yd.

$$= \frac{2}{6}$$
Multiply.

$$= \frac{1}{3}$$
Divide numerator and denominator by their greatest common factor, 2. $\frac{1}{3}$ is read "1 to 3."

Exercises for Example 1

Simplify the ratio.

1. 6 in.:28 in. **2.** $\frac{18 \text{ cm}}{6 \text{ cm}}$ **3.** $\frac{27 \text{ in.}}{3 \text{ ft}}$

Geometry, Concepts and Skills
Practice Workbook with Examples

Reteaching with Practice

For use with pages 357–363

EXAMPLE 2 *Use Ratios*

In the diagram $XY:YZ$ is 1:5 and $XZ = 24$.
Find XY and YZ.

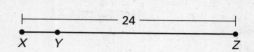

SOLUTION

Let $x = XY$. Because the ratio of XY to YZ is
1 to 5, you know that $YZ = 5x$.

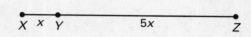

$XY + YZ = XZ$	Segment Addition Postulate
$x + 5x = 24$	Substitute x for XY, $5x$ for YZ, and 24 for XZ.
$6x = 24$	Add like terms.
$x = 4$	Divide each side by 6.

To find XY and YZ, substitute 4 for x.

$XY = x = 4$ $\qquad$ $YZ = 5x = 5 \cdot 4 = 20$

Answer: So, $XY = 4$ and $YZ = 20$.

Exercises for Example 2

Find the segment lengths.

4. In the diagram, $AB:BC$ is 2:1 and $AC = 15$.
Find AB and BC.

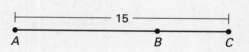

5. In the diagram, $DE:EF$ is 4:9 and $DF = 39$.
Find DE and EF.

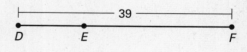

Reteaching with Practice

For use with pages 357–363

6. In the diagram, *JK:KL* is 6:7 and *JL* = 26. Find *JK* and *KL*.

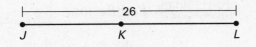

EXAMPLE 3 *Solve a Proportion*

Solve the proportion $\dfrac{3}{2} = \dfrac{9}{x-1}$.

SOLUTION

$$\dfrac{3}{2} = \dfrac{9}{x-1}$$ Write original proportion.

$3(x-1) = 2 \cdot 9$ Cross Product Property

$3x - 3 = 18$ Multiply and use the Distributive Property.

$3x = 21$ Add 3 to each side.

$x = 7$ Divide each side by 3.

Exercises for Example 3

Solve the proportion.

7. $\dfrac{x}{2} = \dfrac{7}{14}$

8. $\dfrac{5}{7} = \dfrac{y+1}{21}$

9. $\dfrac{27}{x-5} = \dfrac{3}{2}$

Geometry, Concepts and Skills
Practice Workbook with Examples

NAME _____ DATE _____

Reteaching with Practice

For use with pages 364–371

CALIFORNIA
Geometry Content Standards
4.0

GOAL Identify similar polygons.

VOCABULARY

Two polygons are **similar polygons** if corresponding angles are congruent and corresponding side lengths are proportional.

If the two polygons are similar, then the ratio of the lengths of two corresponding sides is called the **scale factor**.

Theorem 7.1   Perimeters of Similar Polygons
If two polygons are similar, then the ratio of their perimeters is equal to the ratio of their corresponding side lengths.

EXAMPLE 1 *Use Similarity Statements*

$JKLM \sim WXYZ$

a. List all pairs of congruent angles.

b. Write the ratios of the corresponding sides in a statement of proportionality.

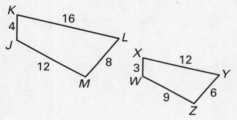

c. Check that the ratios of corresponding sides are equal.

SOLUTION

a. $\angle J \cong \angle W$, $\angle K \cong \angle X$, $\angle L \cong \angle Y$, and $\angle M \cong \angle Z$

b. $\dfrac{WX}{JK} = \dfrac{XY}{KL} = \dfrac{YZ}{LM} = \dfrac{WZ}{JM}$

c. $\dfrac{WX}{JK} = \dfrac{3}{4}, \dfrac{XY}{KL} = \dfrac{12}{16} = \dfrac{3}{4}, \dfrac{YZ}{LM} = \dfrac{6}{8} = \dfrac{3}{4}$, and $\dfrac{WZ}{JM} = \dfrac{9}{12} = \dfrac{3}{4}$

The ratios of corresponding sides are all equal to $\dfrac{3}{4}$.

NAME_____ DATE _____

Reteaching with Practice

For use with pages 364–371

Exercises for Example 1

List all pairs of congruent angles. Write the ratios of the corresponding sides in a statement of proportionality. Then check that the ratios of corresponding sides are equal.

1. $\triangle LMN \sim \triangle RST$

2. $ABCD \sim EFGH$

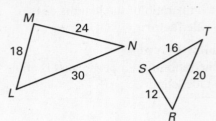

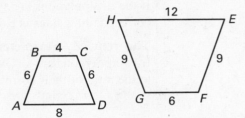

EXAMPLE 2 *Determine whether Polygons are Similar*

Determine whether the quadrilaterals are similar. If they are similar, write a similarity statement and find the scale factor of $FGHE$ to $ABCD$.

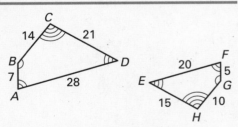

SOLUTION

From the diagram, you know that the corresponding angles are congruent because $\angle A \cong \angle F$, $\angle B \cong \angle G$, $\angle C \cong \angle H$, and $\angle D \cong \angle E$. The corresponding side lengths are proportional because the following ratios are equal.

$$\frac{FG}{AB} = \frac{5}{7} \qquad \frac{GH}{BC} = \frac{10}{14} = \frac{5}{7} \qquad \frac{HE}{CD} = \frac{15}{21} = \frac{5}{7} \qquad \frac{FE}{AD} = \frac{20}{28} = \frac{5}{7}$$

The quadrilaterals are similar. $FGHE \sim ABCD$. The scale factor of $FGHE$ to $ABCD$ is $\frac{5}{7}$.

Geometry, Concepts and Skills
Practice Workbook with Examples

LESSON
7.2
CONTINUED

NAME_____ DATE _____

Reteaching with Practice

For use with pages 364–371

Exercise for Example 2

3. Determine whether the polygons are similar. If they are similar, write a similarity statement and find the scale factor of Figure B to Figure A.

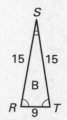

EXAMPLE 3 *Use Similar Polygons*

In the diagram, $JKLM \sim PQRS$.
Find the value of x.

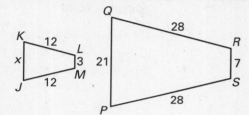

SOLUTION

Because the quadrilaterals are similar, the corresponding side lengths are proportional.

To find the value of x, you can use the following proportion.

$\dfrac{RS}{LM} = \dfrac{PQ}{JK}$ Write proportion.

$\dfrac{7}{3} = \dfrac{21}{x}$ Substitute 7 for RS, 3 for LM, 21 for PQ, and x for JK.

$7x = 63$ Cross Product Property

$x = 9$ Divide each side by 7.

Exercises for Example 3

In the diagram, $\triangle ABC \sim \triangle XYZ$. Find the value of x.

4.

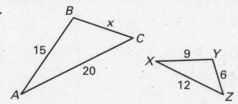

5.

Reteaching with Practice

For use with pages 372–378

CALIFORNIA
Geometry Content Standards 5.0

GOAL Show that two triangles are similar using the AA Similarity

> ## VOCABULARY
>
> **Postulate 15   Angle-Angle (AA) Similarity Postulate**
> If two angles of one triangle are congruent to two angles of another
> triangle, then the two triangles are similar.

EXAMPLE 1 *Use the AA Similarity Postulate*

Determine whether the triangles are similar. If they are
similar, write a similarity statement. Explain your
reasoning.

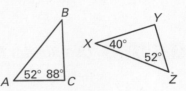

SOLUTION

If two pairs of angles are congruent, then the triangles are similar.
$\angle A \cong \angle Z$ because they both have a measure of 52°. $\angle C$ is not
congruent to $\angle X$ because their measures are not equal (88° ≠ 40°).
So find $m\angle Y$ to see whether $\angle C$ is congruent to $\angle Y$.

$$m\angle Y + 52° + 40° = 180° \qquad \text{Triangle Sum Theorem}$$
$$m\angle Y + 92° = 180° \qquad \text{Add.}$$
$$m\angle Y = 88° \qquad \text{Subtract 92° from each side.}$$

Both $\angle C$ and $\angle Y$ measure 88°, so $\angle C \cong \angle Y$. By the AA Similarity Postulate,
$\triangle ABC \sim \triangle ZXY$.

Exercises for Example 1

**Determine whether the triangles are similar. If they are
similar, write a similarity statement.**

1.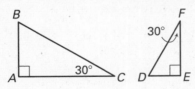

2.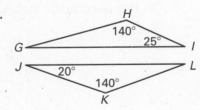

NAME_____ DATE _____

Reteaching with Practice

For use with pages 372–378

3.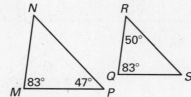

4.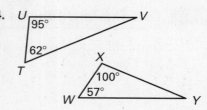

Use the AA Similarity Postulate

Given that $\overline{AE}$ bisects $\angle BAD$, is there enough information to show that $\triangle ABC$ is similar to $\triangle ADE$? Explain your reasoning.

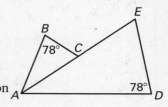

SOLUTION

From the diagram, you know that $\angle B \cong \angle D$. By the definition of an angle bisector, you know that $\angle BAC \cong \angle DAE$.
So, $\triangle ABC \sim \triangle ADE$ by the AA Similarity Postulate.

Exercises for Example 2

Determine whether you can show that the triangles are similar. If so, write a similarity statement. Explain your reasoning.

5. $\overline{KN} \perp \overline{JM}$

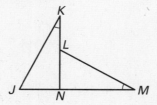

6. $\overline{QP} \parallel \overline{ST}$

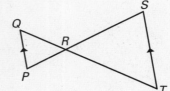

Reteaching with Practice

For use with pages 372–378

EXAMPLE 3 ## *Use Similar Triangles*

In the diagram, $\overline{PQ} \parallel \overline{RS}$ and $\overline{QR} \parallel \overline{ST}$.
Find the value of x.

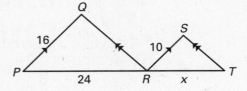

SOLUTION

Corresponding angles of parallel lines are congruent, so $\angle QPR \cong \angle SRT$ and
$\angle QRP \cong \angle STR$. By the AA Similarity Postulate, $\triangle PQR \sim \triangle RST$. To find the
value of x, set up the following proportion.

$\dfrac{RS}{PQ} = \dfrac{RT}{PR}$ Write a proportion.

$\dfrac{10}{16} = \dfrac{x}{24}$ Substitute 10 for RS, 16 for PQ, x for RT, and 24 for PR.

$240 = 16x$ Cross Product Property

$15 = x$ Divide each side by 16.

Exercises for Example 3

**Write a similarity statement for the triangles. Then find the
value of the variable.**

7.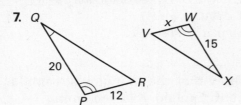

8.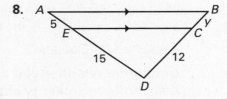

Geometry, Concepts and Skills
Practice Workbook with Examples

Reteaching with Practice

For use with pages 379–385

CALIFORNIA
Geometry Content Standards
5.0

GOAL Show that two triangles are similar using
the SSS and SAS Similarity Theorems.

VOCABULARY

Theorem 7.2   Side-Side-Side (SSS) Similarity Theorem
If the corresponding sides of two triangles are proportional, then the
triangles are similar.

Theorem 7.3   Side-Angle-Side (SAS) Similarity Theorem
If an angle of one triangle is congruent to an angle of a second triangle
and the lengths of the sides that include these angles are proportional,
then the triangles are similar.

EXAMPLE 1   *Use the SSS Similarity Theorem*

Determine whether the triangles are similar.
If they are similar, write a similarity statement
and find the scale factor of $\triangle DEF$ to $\triangle ABC$.

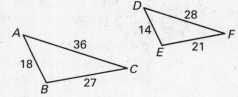

SOLUTION

Find the ratios of the corresponding sides.

$$\frac{DE}{AB} = \frac{14 \div 2}{18 \div 2} = \frac{7}{9}$$

$$\frac{EF}{BC} = \frac{21}{27} = \frac{21 \div 3}{27 \div 3} = \frac{7}{9}$$

$$\frac{DF}{AC} = \frac{28}{36} = \frac{28 \div 4}{36 \div 4} = \frac{7}{9}$$

All three ratios are equal. So, the corresponding sides of the triangles are
proportional. By the SSS Similarity Theorem, $\triangle ABC \sim \triangle DEF$. The scale factor
of $\triangle DEF$ to $\triangle ABC$ is $\frac{7}{9}$.

Exercises for Example 1

**Determine whether the triangles are similar. If they are
similar, write a similarity statement and find the scale factor
of triangle B to triangle A.**

1.

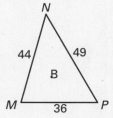

NAME_____ DATE _____

Reteaching with Practice

For use with pages 379–385

2.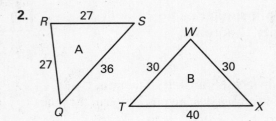

EXAMPLE 2 *Use the SAS Similarity Theorem*

Determine whether the triangles are similar.
If they are similar, write a similarity statement.

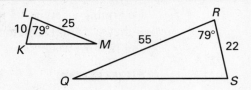

SOLUTION

$\angle L$ and $\angle R$ both measure 79°, so $\angle L \cong \angle R$.
Compare the ratios of the side lengths that
include $\angle L$ and $\angle R$.

Shorter sides: $\dfrac{RS}{LK} = \dfrac{22}{10} = \dfrac{22 \div 2}{10 \div 2} = \dfrac{11}{5}$ Longer sides: $\dfrac{QR}{ML} = \dfrac{55}{25} = \dfrac{55 \div 5}{25 \div 5} = \dfrac{11}{5}$

The lengths of the sides that include $\angle L$ and $\angle R$ are proportional. By the SAS Similarity
Theorem, $\triangle KLM \sim \triangle SRQ$.

Exercises for Example 2

**Determine whether the triangles are similar. If they are
similar, write a similarity statement.**

3.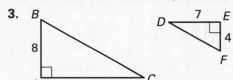

4.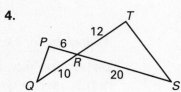

Geometry, Concepts and Skills
Practice Workbook with Examples

NAME_____ DATE _____

Reteaching with Practice

For use with pages 379–385

EXAMPLE 3 *Similarity in Overlapping Triangles*

Show that $\triangle ACD \sim \triangle ABE$.

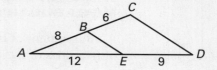

SOLUTION

Separate $\triangle ACD$ and $\triangle ABE$
and label the side lengths.

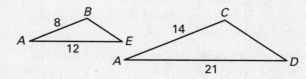

$\angle A \cong \angle A$ by Reflexive Property of Congruence.

Shorter sides: $\dfrac{AC}{AB} = \dfrac{8+6}{8} = \dfrac{14}{8} = \dfrac{7}{4}$ Longer sides: $\dfrac{AD}{AE} = \dfrac{12+9}{12} = \dfrac{21}{12} = \dfrac{7}{4}$

The lengths of the sides that include $\angle A$ are proportional. By the SAS Similarity
Theorem, $\triangle ACD \sim \triangle ABE$.

Exercise for Example 3

5. Show that the overlapping triangles are similar.
Then write a similarity statement.

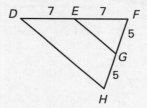

Reteaching with Practice

For use with pages 386–392

CALIFORNIA
Geometry Content Standards
5.0

GOAL Use the Triangle Proportionality Theorem and its converse.

VOCABULARY

A **midsegment of a triangle** is a segment that connects the midpoints of two sides of a triangle.

Theorem 7.4   Triangle Proportionality Theorem
If a line parallel to one side of a triangle intersects the other two sides, then it divides the two sides proportionally.

Theorem 7.5   Converse of the Triangle Proportionality Theorem
If a line divides two sides of a triangle proportionally, then it is parallel to the third side.

Theorem 7.6   The Midsegment Theorem
The segment connecting the midpoints of two sides of a triangle is parallel to the third side and half as long.

EXAMPLE 1   *Find Segment Lengths*

Find the value of *x*.

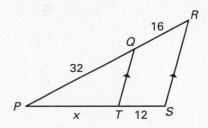

SOLUTION

$$\frac{PQ}{QR} = \frac{PT}{TS} \qquad \text{Triangle Proportionality Theorem}$$

$$\frac{32}{16} = \frac{x}{12} \qquad \text{Substitute 32 for } PQ, \text{16 for } QR, x \text{ for } PT, \text{ and 12 for } TS.$$

$$32 \cdot 12 = 16 \cdot x \qquad \text{Cross Product Property}$$

$$384 = 16x \qquad \text{Multiply.}$$

$$\frac{384}{16} = \frac{16x}{16} \qquad \text{Divide each side by 16.}$$

$$24 = x \qquad \text{Simplify.}$$

NAME_____ DATE_____

Reteaching with Practice

For use with pages 386–392

Exercises for Example 1

Find the value of the variable.

1.
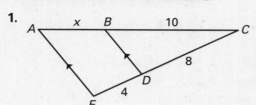

2.
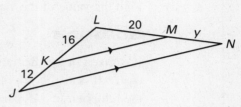

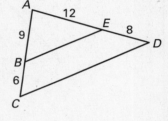

EXAMPLE 2 *Determine Parallels*

Given the diagram, determine whether
$\overline{BE}$ is parallel to $\overline{CD}$.

SOLUTION

Find and simplify the ratios of the two sides divided
by $\overline{BE}$.

$$\frac{AB}{BC} = \frac{9}{6} = \frac{3}{2} \qquad \frac{AE}{ED} = \frac{12}{8} = \frac{3}{2}$$

The ratios are equal, so the two sides divided by $\overline{BE}$ are proportional. By the Converse
of the Triangle Proportionality Theorem, $\overline{BE}$ is parallel to $\overline{CD}$.

Exercises for Example 2

Given the diagram, determine whether $\overline{BE}$ is parallel to $\overline{CD}$. Explain.

3.
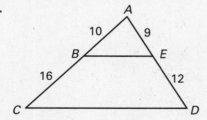

4.
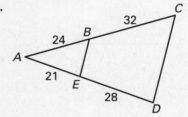

NAME _____ DATE _____

Reteaching with Practice

For use with pages 386–392

EXAMPLE 3 *Use the Midsegment Theorem*

Find the value of the variable.

SOLUTION

It is given in the diagram that $KL = JK = 8$, so K is the midpoint of $\overline{JL}$. It is also given in the diagram that $JN = MN = 10$, so N is the midpoint of $\overline{JM}$. Therefore, $\overline{KN}$ is a midsegment of $\triangle JLM$. Use the Midsegment Theorem to write the following equation.

$KN = \dfrac{1}{2}LM$ The Midsegment Theorem

$13 = \dfrac{1}{2}x$ Substitute 13 for KN and x for LM.

$x = 26$ Multiply each side by 2.

Exercises for Example 3

Find the value of the variable.

5.

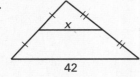

6.

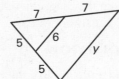

7.

16, x

NAME _____ DATE _____

Reteaching with Practice

For use with pages 393–399

CALIFORNIA
Geometry Content Standards
22.0

GOAL Identify and draw dilations.

VOCABULARY

A **dilation** is a transformation with center C and scale factor k that maps each point P to an image point P' so that P' lies on $\overrightarrow{CP}$ and $CP' = k \cdot CP$.

A dilation is called a **reduction** if the image is smaller than the original figure.

A dilation is called an **enlargement** if the image is larger than the original figure.

EXAMPLE 1 *Identify Dilations*

Tell whether the dilation is a *reduction* or an *enlargement*.

a.
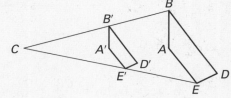

b.
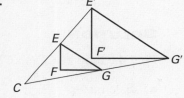

SOLUTION

a. The dilation is a reduction because the image ($A'B'D'E'$) is smaller than the original figure ($ABDE$).

b. The dilation is an enlargement because the image ($\triangle\ E'F'G'$) is larger than the original figure ($\triangle\ EFG$).

Exercises for Example 1

Tell whether the dilation is a *reduction* or an *enlargement*.

1.
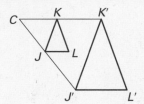

2.
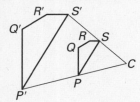

Geometry, Concepts and Skills
Practice Workbook with Examples

133

Reteaching with Practice

For use with pages 393–399

3.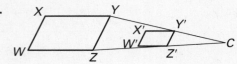

EXAMPLE 2 *Find Scale Factors*

Find the scale factor of the dilation.

a.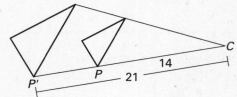

b.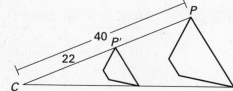

SOLUTION

Find the ratio of CP' to CP.

a. scale factor $= \dfrac{CP'}{CP} = \dfrac{21}{14} = \dfrac{3}{2}$ **b.** scale factor $= \dfrac{CP'}{CP} = \dfrac{22}{40} = \dfrac{11}{20}$

Exercises for Example 2

Find the scale factor of the dilation.

4.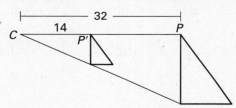

5.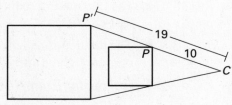

Geometry, Concepts and Skills
Practice Workbook with Examples

NAME _____ DATE _____

Reteaching with Practice

For use with pages 393–399

EXAMPLE 3 *Dilations and Similar Figures*

$\triangle A'P'D'$ is the image of $\triangle APD$ after an enlargement. Find the value of x.

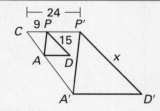

SOLUTION

$\dfrac{CP'}{CP} = \dfrac{P'D'}{PD}$ Write a proportion.

$\dfrac{24}{9} = \dfrac{x}{15}$ Substitute 24 for CP', 9 for CP, x for $P'D'$, and 15 for PD.

$360 = 9x$ Cross Product Property

$40 = x$ Divide each side by 9.

Exercises for Example 3

$\triangle P'S'T'$ **is the image of** $\triangle PST$ **after a dilation. Find the value of** ***x.***

6.

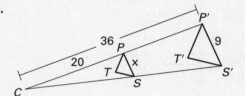

7.

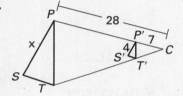

NAME_____ DATE _____

Reteaching with Practice

For use with pages 411– 415

CALIFORNIA
Geometry Content Standards
12.0

GOAL Describe polygons.

VOCABULARY

A polygon is **convex** if no line that contains a side of the polygon passes through the interior of the polygon.

A polygon that is not convex is called **concave**.

A polygon is **equilateral** if all of its sides are congruent.

A polygon is **equiangular** if all of its interior angles are congruent.

A polygon is **regular** if it is both equilateral and equiangular.

EXAMPLE 1 *Identify Convex and Concave Polygons*

Decide whether the polygon is *convex* or *concave*.

a.

b.

SOLUTION

a. None of the extended sides pass through the interior.
   So, the polygon is convex.

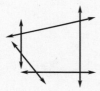

b. At least one extended side passes through the interior.
   So, the polygon is concave.

Exercises for Example 1

Decide whether the polygon is *convex* or *concave*.

1.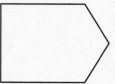

2.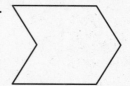

3.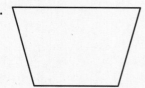

Geometry, Concepts and Skills
Practice Workbook with Examples

Reteaching with Practice

For use with pages 411–415

4. 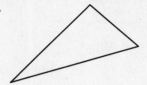 **5.**  **6.**

EXAMPLE 2 *Identify Regular Polygons*

Decide whether the polygon is regular. Explain your answer.

a.   **b.**

SOLUTION

a. The polygon is equilateral because all of the sides are congruent. The polygon is not equiangular because not all of the angles are congruent. So, the polygon is not regular.

b. The polygon is equilateral because all of the sides are congruent. The polygon is equiangular because all of the angles are congruent. So, the polygon is regular.

Exercises for Example 2

Decide whether the polygon is regular. Explain your answer.

7.   **8.** 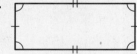 **9.**

Geometry, Concepts and Skills
Practice Workbook with Examples

Reteaching with Practice

For use with pages 411–415

EXAMPLE 3 *Using Algebra*

The polygon is regular. Find the value of x.

SOLUTION

Because the polygon is regular, all of its sides are congruent.

$AB = DE$	The sides of the polygon are congruent.
$25 = 6x + 1$	Substitute 25 for AB and $6x + 1$ for DE.
$24 = 6x$	Subtract 1 from each side.
$4 = x$	Divide each side by 6.

Exercises for Example 3

The polygons are regular. Find the value of x.

10.

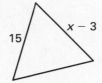

11.

12.

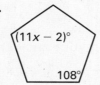

Geometry, Concepts and Skills
Practice Workbook with Examples

NAME _____ DATE _____

Reteaching with Practice

For use with pages 416–423

CALIFORNIA
Geometry Content Standards
12.0

GOAL Find the measures of interior and exterior angles of polygons.

VOCABULARY

Theorem 8.1   Polygon Interior Angles Theorem
The sum of the measures of the interior angles of a convex polygon with n sides is $(n - 2) \cdot 180°$.

Theorem 8.2   Polygon Exterior Angles Theorem
The sum of the measures of the exterior angles of a convex polygon, one angle at each vertex, is 360°.

EXAMPLE 1   *Use Polygon Interior Angles Theorem*

Find the sum of the measures of the interior angles of the polygon.

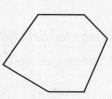

SOLUTION

The polygon has six sides (hexagon). Use the Polygon Interior Angles Theorem and substitute 6 for n.

$$
\begin{aligned}
(n - 2) \cdot 180° = (6 - 2) \cdot 180° \quad &\text{Substitute 6 for } n. \\
= 4 \cdot 180° \quad &\text{Simplify.} \\
= 720° \quad &\text{Multiply.}
\end{aligned}
$$

Exercises for Example 1
....

Find the sum of the measures of the interior angles of the polygon.

1. quadrilateral   **2.** pentagon   **3.** octagon

NAME _____ DATE _____

Reteaching with Practice

For use with pages 416–423

EXAMPLE 2 ***Find the Measure of an Interior Angle***

Find the measure of $\angle A$ in the diagram.

SOLUTION

The polygon has five sides, so the sum of the measures of the interior angles is

$$(n - 2) \cdot 180° = (5 - 2) \cdot 180° = 3 \cdot 180° = 540°.$$

Add the measures of the interior angles and set the sum equal to 540°.

$$90° + 135° + 83° + 96° + m\angle A = 540° \qquad \text{The sum is 540°.}$$
$$404° + m\angle A = 540° \qquad \text{Simplify.}$$
$$m\angle A = 136° \qquad \text{Subtract 404° from each side.}$$

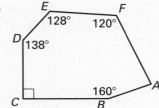

Exercises for Example 2

Find the measure of $\angle A$.

4.

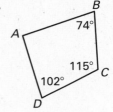

5.

6.

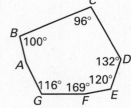

NAME _____ DATE _____

Reteaching with Practice

For use with pages 416–423

EXAMPLE 3 *Find the Measure of an Exterior Angle*

Find the value of *x*.

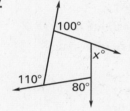

SOLUTION

Using the Polygon Exterior Angles Theorem, set the
sum of the exterior angles equal to 360°.

$130° + x° + 100° + 30° + x° = 360°$	Polygon Exterior Angles Theorem
$260 + 2x = 360$	Add like terms.
$2x = 100$	Subtract 260 from each side.
$x = 50$	Divide each side by 2.

Answer: The value of *x* is 50.

Exercises for Example 3

Find the value of *x*.

7.

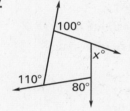

8.

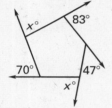

9.

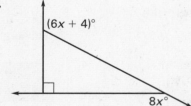

NAME_____ DATE _____

Reteaching with Practice

For use with pages 424–429

CALIFORNIA
Geometry Content Standards
10.0

GOAL Find the area of squares and rectangles.

VOCABULARY

The amount of surface covered by a figure is its **area**.

Area of a Square: Area = (side)^2

Area of a Rectangle: Area = (base)(height)

EXAMPLE 1 *Find the Area of a Square and the Area of a Rectangle*

a. Find the area of the square.

b. Find the area of the rectangle.

 6 in.

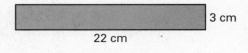 3 cm
22 cm

SOLUTION

a. Use the formula for the area of a square and substitute 6 for *s*.

$A = s^2$ Formula for the area of a square

$= 6^2$ Substitute 6 for *s*.

$= 36$ Simplify.

Answer: The area of the square is 36 square inches.

b. Use the formula for the area of a rectangle and substitute 22 for *b* and 3 for *h*.

$A = bh$ Formula for the area of a rectangle

$= 22 \cdot 3$ Substitute 22 for *b* and 3 for *h*.

$= 66$ Simplify.

Answer: The area of the rectangle is 66 square centimeters.

Exercises for Example 1

Find the area of the square or rectangle.

1. rectangle

10 ft

8 ft

2. square

 4 in.

3. rectangle

6 cm
15 cm

NAME_____ DATE _____

Reteaching with Practice

For use with pages 424–429

EXAMPLE 2 *Find the Base of a Rectangle*

The rectangle has an area of 132 square feet.
Find its base.

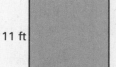

11 ft

SOLUTION

$A = bh$	Formula for the area of a rectangle
$132 = b \cdot 11$	Substitute 132 for A and 11 for h.
$12 = b$	Divide each side by 11.

Answer: The base of the rectangle is 12 feet.

Exercises for Example 2

A gives the area of the rectangle. Find the missing side length.

4.

4 in.

b

$A = 12 \text{ in.}^2$

5.

h

9 ft

$A = 81 \text{ ft}^2$

6.
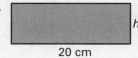

h

20 cm

$A = 140 \text{ cm}^2$

NAME_____ DATE _____

Reteaching with Practice

For use with pages 424–429

EXAMPLE 3 *Find the Area of a Complex Polygon*

Find the area of the polygon made up of rectangles.

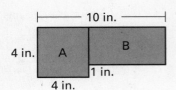

SOLUTION

Add the areas of the two rectangles. Notice that the base and the height of rectangle A are given in the diagram. The base of rectangle B is 10 inches minus 4 inches. The height of rectangle B is 4 inches minus 1 inch.

$$\text{Area} = \text{Area of A} + \text{Area of B}$$
$$= 4 \cdot 4 + (10 - 4) \cdot (4 - 1)$$
$$= 4 \cdot 4 + 6 \cdot 3$$
$$= 16 + 18$$
$$= 34 \text{ in.}^2$$

Exercises for Example 3

Find the area of the polygon made up of rectangles.

7.

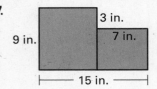

8.

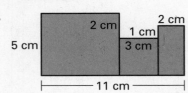

NAME_____ DATE _____

Reteaching with Practice

For use with pages 430–438

CALIFORNIA
Geometry Content Standards
8.0

GOAL Find the area of triangles.

VOCABULARY

The **height of a triangle** is the perpendicular segment from a vertex to the line containing the opposite side, called the **base of the triangle**.

Area of a Triangle: Area $= \frac{1}{2}$(base)(height)

Theorem 8.3   Areas of Similar Polygons

If two polygons are similar with a scale factor of $\frac{a}{b}$, then the ratio of their areas is $\frac{a^2}{b^2}$.

EXAMPLE 1   *Find the Area of a Right Triangle*

Find the area of the right triangle.

SOLUTION

Use the formula for the area of a triangle and substitute 15 for b and 8 for h.

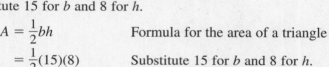

8 yd

15 yd

$$A = \frac{1}{2}bh \qquad \text{Formula for the area of a triangle}$$

$$= \frac{1}{2}(15)(8) \qquad \text{Substitute 15 for } b \text{ and 8 for } h.$$

$$= 60 \qquad \text{Simplify.}$$

Answer: The right triangle has an area of 60 square yards.

Exercises for Example 1

Find the area of the right triangle.

1.

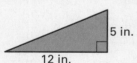

5 in.

12 in.

2.

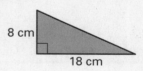

8 cm

18 cm

3.

7 ft

4 ft

Geometry, Concepts and Skills
Practice Workbook with Examples

NAME_____ DATE _____

Reteaching with Practice

For use with pages 430–438

EXAMPLE 2 *Find the Area of a Triangle*

Find the area of the triangle.

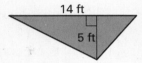

SOLUTION

$A = \frac{1}{2}bh$ Formula for the area of a triangle

$= \frac{1}{2}(8)(4)$ Substitute 8 for b and 4 for h.

$= 16$ Simplify.

Answer: The triangle has an area of 16 square centimeters.

Exercises for Example 2

Find the area of the triangle.

4.

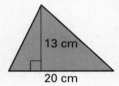

5.

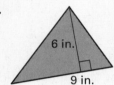

6.

EXAMPLE 3 *Find the Base of a Triangle*

Find the base of the triangle, given that its area
is 42 square feet.

SOLUTION

$A = \frac{1}{2}bh$ Formula for the area of a triangle

$42 = \frac{1}{2}b \cdot 6$ Substitute 42 for A and 6 for h.

$84 = b \cdot 6$ Multiply each side by 2.

$14 = b$ Divide each side by 6.

Answer: The triangle has a base of 14 feet.

NAME_____ DATE _____

Reteaching with Practice

For use with pages 430–438

Exercises for Example 3

A gives the area of the triangle. Find the missing measure.

7. $A = 15$ in.^{2}

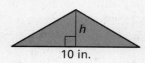

10 in.

8. $A = 126$ cm^2

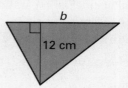

b

12 cm

9. $A = 6$ ft^2

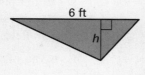

6 ft

h

EXAMPLE 4 *Areas of Similar Triangles*

$\triangle ABC \sim \triangle DEF$. Find the scale factor of $\triangle DEF$ to $\triangle ABC$. Then find the ratio of their areas.

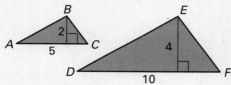

SOLUTION

The scale factor of $\triangle DEF$ to $\triangle ABC$ is $\frac{4}{2} = \frac{2}{1}$. Then by Theorem 8.3, the ratio of the areas of $\triangle DEF$ to $\triangle ABC$ is $\frac{2^2}{1^2} = \frac{4}{1}$. You can verify this by finding their areas.

Exercise for Example 4

10. $\triangle ABC \sim \triangle DEF$. Find the scale factor of $\triangle DEF$ to $\triangle ABC$. Then find the ratio of their areas.

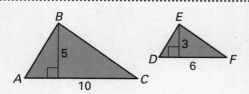

NAME_____ DATE _____

Reteaching with Practice

For use with pages 439–445

CALIFORNIA
Geometry Content Standards
10.0

GOAL Find the area of parallelograms.

VOCABULARY

Either pair of parallel sides of a parallelogram are called the **bases of the parallelogram**. The shortest distance between the bases of a parallelogram is called the **height of a parallelogram**.

Area of a Parallelogram: Area = (base)(height)

Area of a Rhombus: Area = $\frac{1}{2}$(product of diagonals)

EXAMPLE 1 *Find the Area of a Parallelogram*

Find the area of the parallelogram.

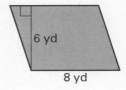

6 yd

8 yd

SOLUTION

Use the formula for the area of a parallelogram and substitute 8 for *b* and 6 for *h*.

$A = bh$ Formula for the area of a parallelogram

$= (8)(6)$ Substitute 8 for *b* and 6 for *h*.

$= 48$ Multiply.

Answer: The parallelogram has an area of 48 square yards.

Exercises for Example 1

Find the area of the parallelogram.

1.

9 m

5 m

2.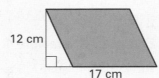

12 cm

17 cm

Geometry, Concepts and Skills
Practice Workbook with Examples

NAME _____ DATE _____

Reteaching with Practice

For use with pages 439–445

3.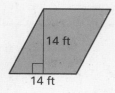

4.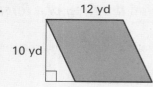

EXAMPLE 2 *Find the Base of a Parallelogram*

Find the base of the parallelogram given that its area
is 105 square inches.

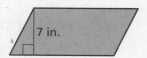

SOLUTION

Use the formula for the area of a parallelogram and
substitute 105 for A and 7 for h.

$A = bh$	Formula for the area of a parallelogram
$105 = b \cdot 7$	Substitute 105 for A and 7 for h.
$15 = b$	Divide each side by 7.

Answer: The parallelogram has a base of 15 inches.

Exercises for Example 2

A gives the area of the parallelogram. Find the missing measure.

5. $A = 63 \text{ m}^2$

6. $A = 144 \text{ ft}^2$

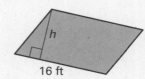

7. $A = 55 \text{ cm}^2$

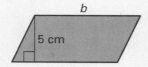

NAME_____ DATE _____

Reteaching with Practice

For use with pages 439–445

EXAMPLE 3 *Find the Area of a Rhombus*

Find the area of the rhombus.

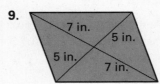

SOLUTION

Use the formula for the area of a rhombus. Add the segment
lengths to find the values of d_1 and d_2.

$$A = \frac{1}{2}d_1d_2 \qquad\qquad \text{Formula for the area of a rhombus}$$

$$= \frac{1}{2}(6 + 6)(3 + 3) \quad \text{Substitute } (6 + 6) \text{ for } d_1 \text{ and } (3 + 3) \text{ for } d_2.$$

$$= \frac{1}{2}(12)(6) \qquad\quad \text{Simplify within parentheses.}$$

$$= 36 \qquad\qquad\quad \text{Multiply.}$$

Answer: The area of the rhombus is 36 square feet.

Exercises for Example 3
....
Find the area of the rhombus.

8.

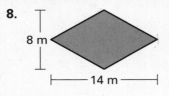

9.

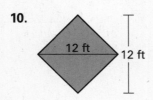

10.

Geometry, Concepts and Skills
Practice Workbook with Examples

Reteaching with Practice

For use with pages 446–450

CALIFORNIA
Geometry Content Standards
10.0, 15.0

GOAL Find the area of trapezoids.

VOCABULARY

The shortest distance between the bases of a trapezoid is the **height of the trapezoid.**

Area of a Trapezoid: Area $= \frac{1}{2}$(height)(sum of bases)

EXAMPLE 1 *Find the Area of a Trapezoid*

Find the area of the trapezoid.

SOLUTION

$A = \frac{1}{2}h(b_1 + b_2)$ Formula for the area of a trapezoid

$= \frac{1}{2}(9)(15 + 13)$ Substitute 9 for h, 15 for b_1, and 13 for b_2.

$= \frac{1}{2}(9)(28)$ Simplify within parentheses.

$= 126 \text{ m}^2$ Multiply.

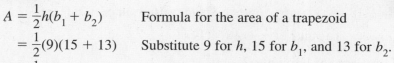

Exercises for Example 1

Find the area of the trapezoid.

1.

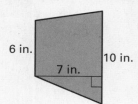

6 in.   10 in.
7 in.

2.   15 cm

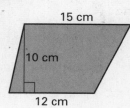

10 cm
12 cm

3.   17 yd

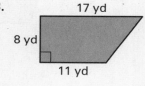

8 yd
11 yd

NAME_____ DATE _____

Reteaching with Practice

For use with pages 446–450

EXAMPLE 2 **Use the Area of a Trapezoid**

Given that the area of the trapezoid
is 170 square inches, find b_1.

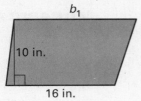

SOLUTION

$A = \frac{1}{2}h(b_1 + b_2)$ Formula for the area of a trapezoid

$170 = \frac{1}{2}(10)(b_1 + 16)$ Substitute 170 for A, 10 for h, and 16 for b_2.

$170 = 5(b_1 + 16)$ Simplify $\frac{1}{2}(10)$.

$34 = b_1 + 16$ Divide each side by 5.

$18 = b_1$ Subtract 16 from each side.

Answer: The value of b_1 is 18 inches.

Exercises for Example 2

A gives the area of the trapezoid. Find the missing measure.

4. $A = 18 \text{ m}^2$

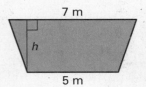

5. $A = 56 \text{ ft}^2$

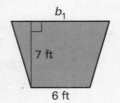

6. $A = 342 \text{ yd}^2$

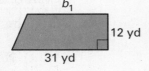

NAME _____ DATE _____

Reteaching with Practice

For use with pages 446–450

EXAMPLE 3 *Use the Pythagorean Theorem*

Find the height using the Pythagorean Theorem.
Then find the area of the trapezoid.

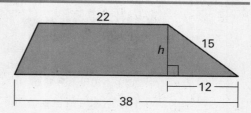

SOLUTION

Find the height of the trapezoid by using the
Pythagorean Theorem on the right triangle.

$$a^2 + b^2 = c^2$$ Pythagorean Theorem

$$h^2 + 12^2 = 15^2$$ Substitute 12 for b, 15 for c, and h for a.

$$h^2 + 144 = 225$$ Simplify.

$$h^2 = 81$$ Subtract 144 from each side.

$$h = 9$$ Take the positive square root of each side.

So, the height of the trapezoid is 9 units. Now use the formula for the
area of the trapezoid.

$$A = \frac{1}{2}h(b_1 + b_2) = \frac{1}{2}(9)(22 + 38) = \frac{1}{2}(9)(60) = 270$$

Answer: The area of the trapezoid is 270 square units.

Exercises for Example 3

**Find the height of the trapezoid using the Pythagorean Theorem.
Then find the area of the trapezoid.**

7.

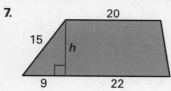

8.

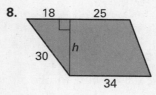

Reteaching with Practice

For use with pages 451–459

CALIFORNIA
Geometry Content Standards

8.0

GOAL Find the circumference and area of circles.

VOCABULARY

A **circle** is the set of all points in a plane that are the same distance from a given point, called the **center** of the circle. The distance from the center to a point on the circle is the **radius**.

The distance across the circle, through the center, is the **diameter**.

The **circumference** of a circle is the distance around the circle.

An angle whose vertex is the center of a circle is a **central angle** of the circle.

A region of a circle determined by two radii and a part of the circle is called a **sector** of the circle.

Circumference of a Circle: Circumference = π (diameter)
                                              = 2π (radius)

Area of a Circle: Area = π (radius)^2

EXAMPLE 1 *Find the Circumference of a Circle*

Find the circumference of the circle.

SOLUTION

Use the formula for the circumference of a circle and substitute 7 for r.

$\quad\quad C = 2\pi r$ $\quad\quad\quad$ Formula for the circumference of a circle

$\quad\quad\quad = 2\pi (7)$ $\quad\quad$ Substitute 7 for r.

$\quad\quad\quad = 14\pi$ $\quad\quad\quad$ Simplify.

$\quad\quad\quad \approx 14(3.14)$ $\quad\quad$ Use 3.14 as an approximation for π.

$\quad\quad\quad = 43.96$ $\quad\quad\quad$ Multiply.

Answer: The circumference of the circle is about 44 meters.

NAME _____ DATE _____

Reteaching with Practice

For use with pages 451–459

Exercises for Example 1

Find the circumference of the circle. Round your answer to the nearest whole number.

1.
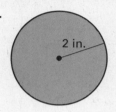
2 in.

2.

11 cm

3.
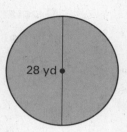
28 yd

EXAMPLE 2 *Find the Area of the Circle*

Find the area of a circle with a radius of 6 feet.

SOLUTION

$A = \pi r^2$ Formula for the area of a circle

$= \pi (6)^2$ Substitute 6 for r.

$= \pi \cdot (36)$ Simplify.

$\approx (3.14) \cdot (36)$ Use 3.14 as an approximation for π.

$\approx 113 \text{ ft}^2$ Multiply.

6 ft

Exercises for Example 2

Find the area of the circle. Round your answer to the nearest whole number.

4.
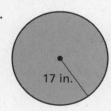
17 in.

5.

5 cm

6.
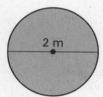
2 m

Geometry, Concepts and Skills
Practice Workbook with Examples

Reteaching with Practice

For use with pages 451–459

EXAMPLE 3 *Find the Area of a Sector*

Find the area of the shaded sector.

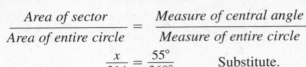

SOLUTION

First find the area of the circle.

$$A = \pi r^2 = \pi (10)^2 \approx 314 \text{ yd}^2$$

Now find the area of the sector. Let x equal the area of the sector.

$$\frac{\text{Area of sector}}{\text{Area of entire circle}} = \frac{\text{Measure of central angle}}{\text{Measure of entire circle}}$$

$\dfrac{x}{314} = \dfrac{55°}{360°}$ Substitute.

$360x = 17{,}270$ Cross product property

$x \approx 48 \text{ yd}^2$ Divide each side by 360.

Exercises for Example 3

Find the area of the shaded sector. Round your answer to the nearest whole number.

7.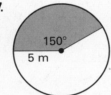

8.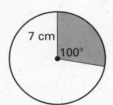

9.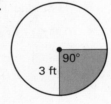

NAME _____ DATE _____

Reteaching with Practice

For use with pages 473–480

GOAL Identify and name solid figures.

VOCABULARY

Three-dimensional shapes are called **solids**.

When a solid is formed by polygons, the solid is called a **polyhedron**.

The plane surfaces of a polyhedron are called **faces**.

The segments joining the vertices of a polyhedron are called **edges**.

The two **bases** of a prism are congruent polygons in parallel planes.

The **base** of a pyramid is a polygon.

EXAMPLE 1 *Identify and Name Polyhedra*

Tell whether the solid is a polyhedron. If so, identify the shape of the bases. Then name the solid.

a.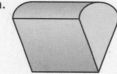

b.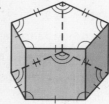

SOLUTION

a. The solid has a curved surface, so it is not a polyhedron.

b. The solid is formed by polygons, so it is a polyhedron. The bases are congruent pentagons in parallel planes. This figure is a pentagonal prism.

Exercises for Example 1

Tell whether the solid is a polyhedron. If so, identify the shape of the bases. Then name the solid.

1.

2.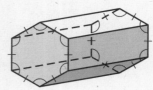

Geometry, Concepts and Skills
Practice Workbook with Examples

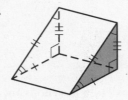

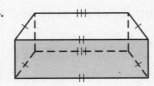

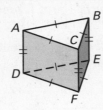

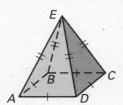

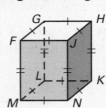

NAME _____ DATE _____

Reteaching with Practice

For use with pages 473–480

3.

4.

EXAMPLE 2 *Find Faces and Edges*

Use the diagram at the right.

a. Name the polyhedron.

b. Count the number of faces and edges.

c. List any congruent faces and congruent edges.

SOLUTION

a. The polyhedron is a triangular prism.

b. The polyhedron has 5 faces and 9 edges.

c. Using the markings on the diagram, you can conclude the following.

Congruent faces:

$\triangle ABC \cong \triangle DEF$

$ACFD \cong CBEF \cong BADE$

Congruent edges:

$\overline{AB} \cong \overline{BC} \cong \overline{AC} \cong \overline{DE} \cong \overline{EF} \cong \overline{DF}$

$\overline{AD} \cong \overline{CF} \cong \overline{BE}$

Exercises for Example 2

Name the polyhedron. Count the number of faces and edges and then list the congruent faces and congruent edges.

5.

6.

NAME _____ DATE _____

Reteaching with Practice

For use with pages 473–480

EXAMPLE 3 *Use Euler's Formula*

Euler's Formula relates the number of faces (F), vertices (V), and edges (E) of a polyhedron by the equation $F + V = E + 2$. Use Euler's Formula to find the number of vertices on the hexagonal pyramid shown.

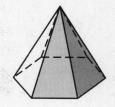

SOLUTION

The hexagonal pyramid has 7 faces and 12 edges.

$F + V = E + 2$	Euler's Formula
$7 + V = 12 + 2$	Substitute 7 for F and 12 for E.
$7 + V = 14$	Simplify.
$V = 7$	Subtract 7 from each side.

Answer: The hexagonal pyramid has 7 vertices.

Exercises for Example 3

Use Euler's Formula to find the number of faces, edges, or vertices.

7. A pyramid has 9 faces and 9 vertices. How many edges does it have?

8. A prism has 8 faces and 18 edges. How many vertices does it have?

9. A polyhedron has 15 edges and 7 vertices. How many faces does it have?

NAME _____ DATE _____

Reteaching with Practice

For use with pages 481–490

CALIFORNIA
Geometry Content Standards
9.0

GOAL Find the surface areas of prisms and cylinders.

VOCABULARY

A **prism** is a polyhedron with two congruent faces that lie in parallel planes.

The **surface area** of a polyhedron is the sum of the areas of its faces.

The **lateral faces** of a prism are the faces of the prism that are not bases.

The **lateral area** of a prism is the sum of the areas of the lateral faces.

A **cylinder** is a solid with two congruent circular bases that lie in parallel planes.

Surface Area of a Prism
Surface area = 2(area of base) + (perimeter of base)(height) = $2B + Ph$

Surface Area of a Cylinder
Surface area = 2(area of base) + (circumference of base)(height) = $2\pi r^2 + 2\pi rh$

EXAMPLE 1 *Use the Net of a Prism*

Find the surface area of the triangular prism.

SOLUTION

If you visualize unfolding the prism and laying it flat, the flat representation of the prism is called a *net*. The surface area of a prism is equal to the area of the net. So, to find the surface area of this triangular prism, you add the areas of the triangles and rectangles that make up the net.

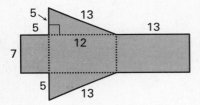

The top face and the bottom face are congruent triangles. Area: $\frac{1}{2}(12)(5) = 30$

The front face is a rectangle. Area: $(12)(7) = 84$

The side face is a rectangle. Area: $(5)(7) = 35$

The back face is a rectangle. Area: $(13)(7) = 91$

$S = 30 + 30 + 84 + 35 + 91 = 270$ Add the area of all five faces.

Answer: The surface area of the prism is 270 square units.

Geometry, Concepts and Skills
Practice Workbook with Examples

Reteaching with Practice

For use with pages 481–490

Exercises for Example 1

Draw the net of the prism in the diagram. Then find the surface area of the prism.

1.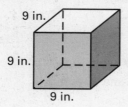
9 in.
9 in.
9 in.

2.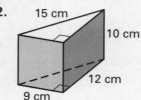
15 cm
10 cm
12 cm
9 cm

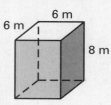

EXAMPLE 2 *Find Surface Area of a Prism*

Find the surface area of the prism.

6 m
6 m
8 m

SOLUTION

Use the formula: Surface area = 2(area of base) + (perimeter of base)(height)
The base of the prism is a square with side length 6. So, (area of base) = 6^2 = 36.
The perimeter of the base is 6 + 6 + 6 + 6 = 24.
The height of the prism is 8.
Surface area = 2(36) + (24)(8) = 72 + 192 = 264

Answer: The surface area of the prism is 264 square meters.

Exercises for Example 2

Find the surface area of the prism.

3.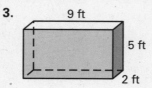
9 ft
5 ft
2 ft

4.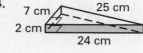
7 cm   25 cm
2 cm
24 cm

5.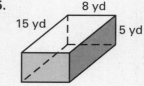
8 yd
15 yd
5 yd

NAME _____ DATE _____

Reteaching with Practice

For use with pages 482–490

EXAMPLE 3 *Find Surface Area of a Cylinder*

Find the surface area of the cylinder. Round your answer
to the nearest whole number.

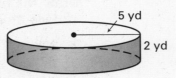

5 yd

2 yd

SOLUTION

$$S = 2\pi r^2 + 2\pi rh \qquad \text{Write the formula for surface area.}$$
$$= 2\pi (5)^2 + 2\pi (5)(2) \qquad \text{Substitute 5 for } r \text{ and 2 for } h.$$
$$= 50\pi + 20\pi \qquad \text{Simplify.}$$
$$= 70\pi \qquad \text{Add.}$$
$$\approx 220 \qquad \text{Multiply.}$$

Answer: The surface area of the cylinder is about 220 square yards.

Exercises for Example 3 ....

**Find the surface area of the cylinder. Round your answer to
the nearest whole number.**

6.   11 m

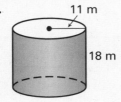

18 m

7. ⊢——— 30 ft ———⊣

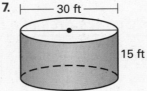

15 ft

8.   6 in.

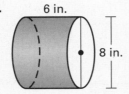

8 in.

Geometry, Concepts and Skills
Practice Workbook with Examples

NAME _____ DATE _____

Reteaching with Practice

For use with pages 491–499

CALIFORNIA
Geometry Content Standards
9.0

GOAL Find the surface areas of pyramids and cones.

VOCABULARY

A **pyramid** is a polyhedron in which the base is a polygon and the lateral faces are triangles with a common vertex.

The **height of a pyramid** is the perpendicular distance between the vertex and base.

The **slant height of a pyramid** is the height of any of its lateral faces.

A **cone** has a circular base and a vertex that is not in the same plane as the base.

The **height of a cone** is the perpendicular distance between the vertex and the base.

The **slant height of a cone** is the distance between the vertex and a point on the base edge.

Surface Area of a Pyramid
Surface area = (area of base) + $\frac{1}{2}$(perimeter of base)(slant height) = $B + \frac{1}{2}P\ell$

Surface Area of a Cone
Surface area = (area of base) + π (radius of base)(slant height) = $\pi r^2 + \pi r\ell$

EXAMPLE 1 *Find the Slant Height*

Find the slant height of the cone. Round your answer to the nearest whole number.

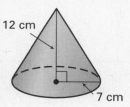

12 cm

7 cm

SOLUTION

The slant height is the length of the hypotenuse of the triangle formed by the height and the radius.

$(slant\ height)^2 = (height)^2 + (radius)^2$ Use the Pythagorean Theorem.

$= 12^2 + 7^2$ Substitute 12 for height and 7 for radius.

$= 144 + 49$ Multiply.

$= 193$ Simplify.

$slant\ height \approx 13.89$ Take the positive square root of each side.

Answer: The slant height of the cone is about 14 centimeters.

NAME_____ DATE _____

Reteaching with Practice

For use with pages 491–499

Exercises for Example 1

Find the slant height of the pyramid or cone. Round your answer to the nearest whole number.

1.

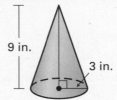

9 in.

3 in.

2.

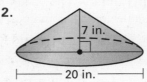

7 in.

20 in.

3.

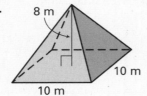

8 m

10 m

10 m

EXAMPLE 2 *Find the Surface Area of a Pyramid*

Find the surface area of the pyramid. Round your answer to the nearest whole number.

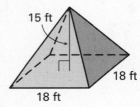

15 ft

18 ft

18 ft

SOLUTION

First, find the area of the base. $B = 18 \times 18 = 324$

Then find the perimeter of the base. $P = 18 + 18 + 18 + 18 = 72$

Then find the slant height.

$(slant\ height)^2 = (height)^2 + (\tfrac{1}{2}side)^2$ Use the Pythagorean Theorem.

$\qquad\qquad = 15^2 + 9^2$ Substitute. Half of 18 is 9.

$\qquad\qquad = 306$ Simplify.

$slant\ height \approx 17.49$ Take positive square root of each side.

Then substitute values into the formula for surface area of a pyramid.

$S = B + \tfrac{1}{2}P\ell$ Write the formula for surface area of a pyramid.

$\approx 324 + \tfrac{1}{2}(72)(17.49)$ Substitute.

$\approx 954\ ft^2$ Simplify.

Geometry, Concepts and Skills
Practice Workbook with Examples

NAME _____ DATE _____

Reteaching with Practice

For use with pages 491–499

Exercise for Example 2

4. Find the surface area of the pyramid. Round your answer to the nearest whole number.

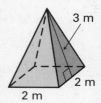

3 m

2 m

2 m

EXAMPLE 3 **Find the Surface Area of a Cone**

Find the surface area of the cone with a radius of 7 centimeters and a slant height of 12 centimeters. Round your answer to the nearest whole number.

SOLUTION

$$S = \pi r^2 + \pi r\ell \qquad \text{Write the formula for surface area of a cone.}$$
$$= \pi (7)^2 + \pi (7)(12) \qquad \text{Substitute.}$$
$$\approx 418 \text{ cm}^2 \qquad \text{Simplify.}$$

Exercise for Example 3

5. Find the surface area of the cone. Round your answer to the nearest whole number.

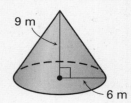

9 m

6 m

NAME _____ DATE _____

Reteaching with Practice

For use with pages 500–507

CALIFORNIA
Geometry Content Standards
9.0

GOAL Find the volumes of prisms and cylinders.

VOCABULARY

The **volume** of a solid is the number of cubic units contained in its interior.

Volume of a Prism
Volume = (area of base)(height) = Bh

Volume of a Cylinder
Volume = (area of base)(height) = $\pi r^2 h$

EXAMPLE 1 *Find the Volume of a Prism*

Find the volume of the prism.

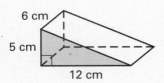

SOLUTION

$V = Bh$ Write the formula for volume of a prism.

$= \left(\dfrac{1}{2} \cdot 5 \cdot 12 \right) \cdot 6$ Area of triangular base $= \dfrac{1}{2} \cdot 5 \cdot 12$.

$= 180$ Simplify.

Answer: The volume of the triangular prism is 180 cubic centimeters.

Exercises for Example 1

Find the volume of the prism.

1.

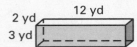

2.

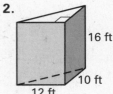

3.

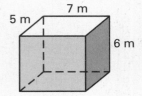

NAME _____ DATE _____

Reteaching with Practice

For use with pages 500–507

EXAMPLE 2 *Find the Volume of a Cylinder*

Find the volume of the cylinder. Round your
answer to the nearest whole number.

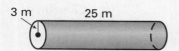

SOLUTION

$V = \pi r^2 h$ Write the formula for volume of a cylinder.

$\quad = \pi (3^2)(25)$ Substitute 3 for r and 25 for h.

$\quad = 225\pi$ Simplify.

$\quad \approx 706.9$ Multiply.

Answer: The volume of the cylinder is about 707 cubic meters.

Exercises for Example 2

**Find the volume of the cylinder. Round your answer to the
nearest whole number.**

4.

5.

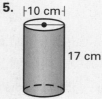

6.

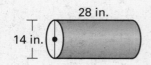

Reteaching with Practice

For use with pages 500–507

EXAMPLE 3 *Using Combined Prisms*

Find the volume of the combined prisms.

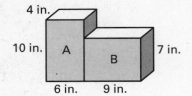

SOLUTION

Find the volume of each prism, and then add the
values to find the volume of the solid.

Volume of prism A:

$V = Bh$	Write the formula for volume of a prism.
$= (6 \cdot 4) \cdot 10$	Area of rectangular base is $6 \cdot 4$.
$= 240$	Simplify.

Volume of prism B:

$V = Bh$	Write the formula for volume of a prism.
$= (9 \cdot 4) \cdot 7$	Area of rectangular base is $9 \cdot 4$.
$= 252$	Simplify.

Add the two values to find the volume of the entire solid.

$$V = 240 + 252 = 492$$

Answer: The volume of the combined prisms is 492 cubic inches.

Exercises for Example 3

Find the volume of the combined prisms.

7.

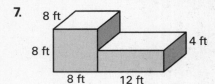

8.

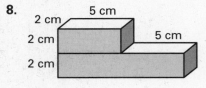

Geometry, Concepts and Skills
Practice Workbook with Examples

NAME_____ DATE _____

Reteaching with Practice

For use with pages 508–516

CALIFORNIA
Geometry Content Standards

9.0

GOAL Find the volumes of pyramids and cones.

VOCABULARY

Volume of a Pyramid

Volume = $\frac{1}{3}$(area of base)(height) = $\frac{1}{3}Bh$

Volume of a Cone

Volume = $\frac{1}{3}$(area of base)(height) = $\frac{1}{3}\pi r^2 h$

EXAMPLE 1 *Find the Volume of a Pyramid*

Find the volume of the pyramid.

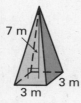

7 m

3 m

3 m

SOLUTION

$V = \frac{1}{3}Bh$ Write the formula for volume of a pyramid.

$= \frac{1}{3}(3^2)(7)$ Area of square base = 3^2.

$= 21 \text{ m}^3$ Simplify.

Exercises for Example 1

Find the volume of the pyramid.

1.

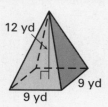

12 yd

9 yd

9 yd

2.

8 m

4 m

6 m

3.

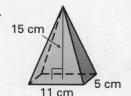

15 cm

11 cm

5 cm

Reteaching with Practice

For use with pages 508–516

EXAMPLE 2 *Find the Volume of a Cone*

Find the volume of the cone. Round your answer to
the nearest whole number.

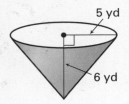

5 yd

6 yd

SOLUTION

$V = \frac{1}{3}\pi r^2 h$ Write the formula for volume of a cone.

$= \frac{1}{3}\pi (5)^2(6)$ Substitute 5 for r and 6 for h.

$\approx 157 \text{ yd}^3$ Multiply.

Exercises for Example 2

**Find the volume of the cone. Round your answer to the
nearest whole number.**

4.

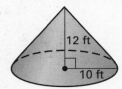

12 ft

10 ft

5. 6 m

8 m

6.

21 cm

14 cm

Reteaching with Practice

For use with pages 508–516

EXAMPLE 3 *Find the Volume of a Pyramid*

Find the volume of the pyramid.

SOLUTION

You are given the slant height of the pyramid.
You need to find the height before you can find
the volume. The height, $\frac{1}{2}$ of one of the sides of
the base, and the slant height form a right triangle.

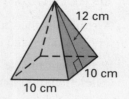

$\left(\frac{1}{2} \; base \; side\right)^2 + (height)^2 = (slant \; height)^2$ Use the Pythagorean Theorem.

$\left(\frac{1}{2} \cdot 10\right)^2 + h^2 = 12^2$ Substitute.

$25 + h^2 = 144$ Simplify.

$h^2 = 119$ Subtract 25 from each side.

$h \approx 10.9$ Take positive square root of each side.

Now find the volume of the pyramid.

$V = \frac{1}{3}Bh$ Write the formula for volume of pyramid.

$\approx \frac{1}{3}(10^2)(10.9)$ Area of square base = 10^2.

≈ 363.3 Simplify.

Answer: The volume of the pyramid is about 363 cubic centimeters.

Exercises for Example 3

**Find the volume of the solid. Round your answer to the
nearest whole number.**

7.

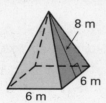

8.

9.

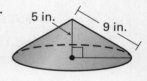

NAME _____ DATE _____

Reteaching with Practice

For use with pages 517–523

CALIFORNIA
Geometry Content Standards
9.0

GOAL Find surface areas and volumes of spheres.

VOCABULARY

A **sphere** is the set of all points in space that are the same distance from a point, called the center of the sphere.

A geometric plane passing through the center of a sphere divides the sphere into two **hemispheres**.

Surface Area of a Sphere

Surface Area $= 4\pi \,(\text{radius})^2 = 4\pi r^2$

Volume of a Sphere

Volume $= \dfrac{4}{3}\pi \,(\text{radius})^3 = \dfrac{4}{3}\pi r^3$

EXAMPLE 1 *Find the Surface Area of a Sphere*

Find the surface area of the sphere. Round your answer to the nearest whole number.

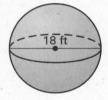

SOLUTION

You are given the diameter of the sphere, which is 18 feet. You need the radius of the sphere to use the formula for surface area. The diameter is 18, so the radius is 9.

$$
\begin{aligned}
S &= 4\pi r^2 &&\text{Write the formula for surface area of a sphere.}\\
&= 4\pi (9)^2 &&\text{Substitute 9 for } r.\\
&\approx 1018 \text{ ft}^2 &&\text{Multiply.}
\end{aligned}
$$

Exercises for Example 1

Find the surface area of the sphere. Round your answer to the nearest whole number.

1.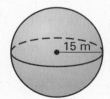

2.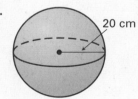

NAME _____ DATE _____

Reteaching with Practice

For use with pages 517–523

3.

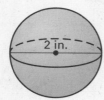

4.

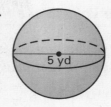

EXAMPLE 2 *Find the Volume of a Sphere*

Find the volume of the sphere. Round your
answer to the nearest whole number.

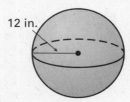

SOLUTION

$V = \frac{4}{3}\pi r^3$ Write the formula for volume of a sphere.

$= \frac{4}{3}\pi (12)^3$ Substitute 12 for *r*.

$\approx 7238 \text{ in.}^3$ Multiply.

Exercises for Example 2

Find the volume of the sphere. Round your answer to the nearest whole number.

5.

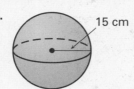

6.

7.

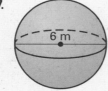

NAME_____ DATE _____

Reteaching with Practice

For use with pages 517–523

EXAMPLE 3 *Find the Volume of a Hemisphere*

Find the volume of the hemisphere. Round your
answer to the nearest whole number.

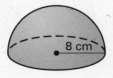

SOLUTION

A hemisphere has half the volume of a sphere.

$$V = \frac{1}{2}\left(\frac{4}{3}\pi r^3\right)$$ Write the formula for $\frac{1}{2}$ the volume of a sphere.

$$= \frac{1}{2}\left(\frac{4}{3}\cdot \pi \cdot 8^3\right)$$ Substitute 8 for r.

$$\approx 1072 \text{ cm}^3$$ Multiply.

Exercises for Example 3

**Find the volume of the hemisphere. Round your answer to the
nearest whole number.**

8.

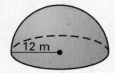

9.

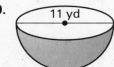

10.

Geometry, Concepts and Skills
Practice Workbook with Examples

Reteaching with Practice

For use with pages 537–541

CALIFORNIA
Geometry Content Standards
15.0

GOAL Simplify square roots.

VOCABULARY

An expression written with a radical symbol is called a *radical expression*, or **radical**. The number or expression inside the radical symbol is the **radicand**.

EXAMPLE 1 *Use a Calculator to Find Square Roots*

Find the square root of 95. Round your answer to the nearest tenth. Check that your answer is reasonable.

SOLUTION

Use your calculator and the following keystrokes.

Calculator Keystrokes	Display	Rounded value
95 $\sqrt{}$ or $\sqrt{}$ 95 **ENTER**	9.74679	$\sqrt{95} \approx 9.7$

This is reasonable because 95 is between the perfect squares 81 and 100. So, $\sqrt{95}$ should be between $\sqrt{81} = 9$ and $\sqrt{100} = 10$. The answer 9.7 is between 9 and 10. Furthermore, $(9.7)^2 = 94.09$, which is close to the original value of 95.

Exercises for Example 1

Find the square root. Round your answer to the nearest tenth. Check that your answer is reasonable.

1. $\sqrt{14}$ **2.** $\sqrt{60}$ **3.** $\sqrt{23}$

4. $\sqrt{115}$ **5.** $\sqrt{72}$ **6.** $\sqrt{155}$

Reteaching with Practice

For use with pages 537–541

EXAMPLE 2 *Find Side Lengths*

Use the Pythagorean Theorem to find the length of the hypotenuse to the nearest tenth.

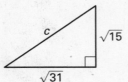

SOLUTION

$$a^2 + b^2 = c^2 \qquad \text{Write the Pythagorean Theorem.}$$
$$(\sqrt{31})^2 + (\sqrt{15})^2 = c^2 \qquad \text{Substitute } \sqrt{31} \text{ for } a \text{ and } \sqrt{15} \text{ for } b.$$
$$31 + 15 = c^2 \qquad \text{Simplify.}$$
$$46 = c^2 \qquad \text{Add.}$$
$$\sqrt{46} = c \qquad \text{Take the square root of each side.}$$
$$6.8 \approx c \qquad \text{Use a calculator.}$$

Exercises for Example 2

Find the missing side length of the right triangle. Round your answer to the nearest tenth.

7.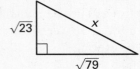

8.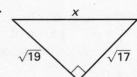

9.

EXAMPLE 3 *Multiply Radicals*

Multiply the radicals. Then simplify if possible.

a. $\sqrt{5} \cdot \sqrt{6}$ **b.** $\sqrt{21} \cdot \sqrt{6}$ **c.** $4\sqrt{5} \cdot \sqrt{10}$

SOLUTION

a. $\sqrt{5} \cdot \sqrt{6} = \sqrt{5 \cdot 6} = \sqrt{30}$

b. $\sqrt{21} \cdot \sqrt{6} = \sqrt{21 \cdot 6} = \sqrt{126} = \sqrt{9 \cdot 14} = \sqrt{9} \cdot \sqrt{14} = 3\sqrt{14}$

c. $4\sqrt{5} \cdot \sqrt{10} = 4 \cdot \sqrt{5 \cdot 10} = 4 \cdot \sqrt{50} = 4 \cdot \sqrt{25 \cdot 2} = 4 \cdot \sqrt{25} \cdot \sqrt{2} = 4 \cdot 5 \cdot \sqrt{2} = 20\sqrt{2}$

Geometry, Concepts and Skills
Practice Workbook with Examples

Reteaching with Practice

Exercises for Example 3

Multiply the radicals. Then simplify if possible.

10. $\sqrt{3} \cdot \sqrt{12}$

11. $\sqrt{10} \cdot \sqrt{33}$

12. $\sqrt{2} \cdot \sqrt{75}$

13. $\sqrt{12} \cdot \sqrt{2}$

14. $\sqrt{50} \cdot \sqrt{10}$

15. $5\sqrt{20} \cdot \sqrt{4}$

EXAMPLE 4 *Square a Radical Expression*

Evaluate the expression.

a. $(4\sqrt{6})^2$ **b.** $(10\sqrt{2})^2$

SOLUTION

a. $(4\sqrt{6})^2 = 4\sqrt{6} \cdot 4\sqrt{6}$ **b.** $(10\sqrt{2})^2 = 10\sqrt{2} \cdot 10\sqrt{2}$

$\phantom{(4\sqrt{6})^2} = 4 \cdot 4 \cdot \sqrt{6} \cdot \sqrt{6}$ $\phantom{(10\sqrt{2})^2} = 10 \cdot 10 \cdot \sqrt{2} \cdot \sqrt{2}$

$\phantom{(4\sqrt{6})^2} = 16 \cdot 6$ $\phantom{(10\sqrt{2})^2} = 100 \cdot 2$

$\phantom{(4\sqrt{6})^2} = 96$ $\phantom{(10\sqrt{2})^2} = 200$

Exercises for Example 4

Evaluate the expression.

16. $(7\sqrt{5})^2$

17. $(6\sqrt{4})^2$

18. $(8\sqrt{2})^2$

NAME _____ DATE _____

Reteaching with Practice

For use with pages 542–547

CALIFORNIA
Geometry Content Standards
20.0

GOAL Find the side lengths of 45°–45°–90° triangles.

VOCABULARY

A right triangle with angle measures of 45°, 45°, and 90° is called a
45°–45°–90° triangle.

Theorem 10.1 45°–45°–90° Triangle Theorem
In a 45°–45°–90° triangle, the length of the hypotenuse is the length of a
leg times $\sqrt{2}$.

EXAMPLE 1 *Find Hypotenuse Length*

Find the length x of the hypotenuse in the 45°–45°–90°
triangle shown at the right.

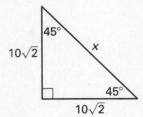

SOLUTION

By the 45°–45°–90° Triangle Theorem, the length of the
hypotenuse is the length of a leg times $\sqrt{2}$.

hypotenuse = leg · $\sqrt{2}$	45°–45°–90° Triangle Theorem
$x = 10\sqrt{2} \cdot \sqrt{2}$	Substitute x for hypotenuse and $10\sqrt{2}$ for leg.
$x = 10 \cdot \sqrt{4}$	Product Property of Radicals
$x = 10 \cdot 2$	Evaluate the square root.
$x = 20$	Simplify.

Answer: The length of the hypotenuse is 20.

Exercises for Example 1

Find the value of *x*.

1.
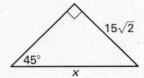

2.
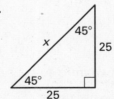

3.
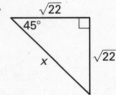

NAME_____ DATE _____

Reteaching with Practice

For use with pages 542–547

EXAMPLE 2 *Find Leg Length*

Find the length x of the leg in the 45°–45°–90° triangle
shown at the right.

SOLUTION

By the 45°–45°–90° Triangle Theorem, the length of the hypotenuse
is the length of a leg times $\sqrt{2}$.

$$\text{hypotenuse} = \text{leg} \cdot \sqrt{2} \qquad \text{45°–45°–90° Triangle Theorem}$$

$$9\sqrt{2} = x\sqrt{2} \qquad \text{Substitute } 9\sqrt{2} \text{ for hypotenuse and } x \text{ for leg.}$$

$$\frac{9\sqrt{2}}{\sqrt{2}} = \frac{x\sqrt{2}}{\sqrt{2}} \qquad \text{Divide each side by } \sqrt{2}.$$

$$9 = x \qquad \text{Simplify.}$$

Exercises for Example 2

Find the value of x.

4.

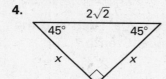

5.

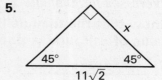

6.

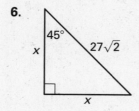

Reteaching with Practice

For use with pages 542–547

EXAMPLE 3 *Find Leg Length*

Show that the triangle is a 45°–45°–90° triangle. Then find the value of *x*. Round your answer to the nearest tenth.

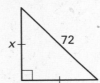

SOLUTION

The triangle is an isosceles right triangle. By the Base Angles Theorem, its acute angles are congruent. The acute angles of a right triangle are complementary. Because the two acute angles are congruent, the measure of each must be 45°. Therefore the triangle is a 45°–45°–90° triangle. You can use the 45°–45°–90° Triangle Theorem to find the value of *x*.

hypotenuse = leg · $\sqrt{2}$	45°–45°–90° Triangle Theorem
$17 = x\sqrt{2}$	Substitute 17 for hypotenuse and *x* for leg.
$\dfrac{17}{\sqrt{2}} = x$	Divide each side by $\sqrt{2}$.
$12.0 \approx x$	Use a calculator to approximate.

Exercises for Example 3

Show that the triangle is a 45°–45°–90° triangle. Then find the value of *x*. Round your answer to the nearest tenth.

7.

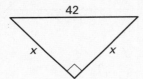

8.

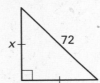

9.

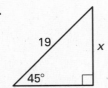

Geometry, Concepts and Skills
Practice Workbook with Examples

NAME _____ DATE _____

Reteaching with Practice

For use with pages 548–555

CALIFORNIA
Geometry Content Standards
20.0

GOAL Find the side lengths of 30°–60°–90° triangles.

VOCABULARY

A right triangle with angle measures of 30°, 60°, and 90° is called a **30°–60°–90° triangle**.

Theorem 10.2   30°–60°–90° Triangle Theorem
In a 30°–60°–90° triangle, the hypotenuse is twice as long as the shorter leg, and the longer leg is the length of the shorter leg times $\sqrt{3}$.

EXAMPLE 1 *Find the Hypotenuse Length*

In the 30°–60°–90° triangle at the right, the length of the shorter leg is given. Find the length of the hypotenuse x.

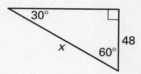

SOLUTION

The hypotenuse of a 30°–60°–90° triangle is twice as long as the shorter leg.

hypotenuse = 2 · shorter leg	30°–60°–90° Triangle Theorem
$x = 2 \cdot 48$	Substitute x for hypotenuse and 48 for shorter leg.
$x = 96$	Simplify.

Answer: The length of the hypotenuse is 96.

Exercises for Example 1
Find the length x of the hypotenuse of the triangle.

1.
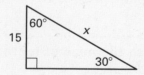

2.

3.
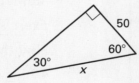

NAME_____ DATE _____

Reteaching with Practice

For use with pages 548–555

EXAMPLE 2 *Find Leg Length*

a. In the 30°–60°–90° triangle at the right, the length of the longer leg is given. Find the length of the shorter leg *x*. Round your answer to the nearest tenth.

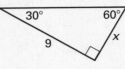

b. In the 30°–60°–90° triangle at the right, the length of the shorter leg is given. Find the length of the longer leg *y*. Round your answer to the nearest tenth.

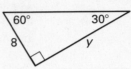

SOLUTION

a. The length of the longer leg of a 30°–60°–90° triangle is the length of the shorter leg times $\sqrt{3}$.

longer leg = shorter leg · $\sqrt{3}$	30°–60°–90° Triangle Theorem
$9 = x\sqrt{3}$	Substitute 9 for longer leg and *x* for shorter leg.
$\dfrac{9}{\sqrt{3}} = x$	Divide each side by $\sqrt{3}$.
$5.2 \approx x$	Use a calculator.

Answer: The length of the shorter leg is about 5.2.

b. The length of the longer leg of a 30°–60°–90° triangle is the length of the shorter leg times $\sqrt{3}$.

longer leg = shorter leg · $\sqrt{3}$	30°–60°–90° Triangle Theorem
$y = 8 \cdot \sqrt{3}$	Substitute *y* for longer leg and 8 for shorter leg.
$y \approx 13.9$	Use a calculator.

Answer: The length of the longer leg is about 13.9.

Exercises for Example 2

Find the value of *x*. Round your answer to the nearest tenth.

4.

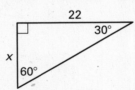

5.

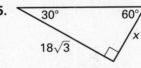

6.

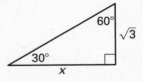

Geometry, Concepts and Skills
Practice Workbook with Examples

Reteaching with Practice

For use with pages 548–555

EXAMPLE 3 *Find Leg Lengths*

Find the length x of the shorter leg and the length
y of the longer leg. Write your answer in radical form.

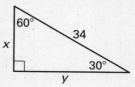

SOLUTION

Use the 30°–60°–90° Triangle Theorem to find the length of the
shorter leg. Then use that value to find the length of the longer leg.

Shorter leg	*Longer leg*
hypotenuse $= 2 \cdot$ shorter leg	longer leg $=$ shorter leg $\cdot \sqrt{3}$
$34 = 2 \cdot x$	$y = 17 \cdot \sqrt{3}$
$17 = x$	$y = 17\sqrt{3}$

Exercises for Example 3

Find the value of each variable. Write your answers in radical form.

7.

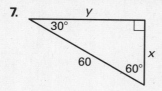

8.

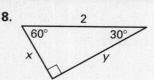

9.

NAME_____ DATE _____

Reteaching with Practice

For use with pages 556–562

GOAL Find the tangent of an acute angle.

VOCABULARY

A **trigonometric ratio** is a ratio of the lengths of two sides of a right triangle. For any acute angle of a right triangle, there is a **leg opposite** the angle and a **leg adjacent** to the angle. The ratio of the leg opposite the angle to the leg adjacent to the angle is the **tangent** of the angle.

Tangent Ratio: $\tan A = \dfrac{\text{leg opposite } \angle A}{\text{leg adjacent to } \angle A}$

EXAMPLE 1 *Find Tangent Ratio*

Find tan D and tan E as fractions in simplified form and as decimals rounded to four decimal places.

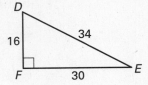

SOLUTION

$\tan D = \dfrac{\text{leg opposite } \angle D}{\text{leg adjacent to } \angle D} = \dfrac{30}{16} = \dfrac{15}{8} = 1.875$

$\tan E = \dfrac{\text{leg opposite } \angle E}{\text{leg adjacent to } \angle E} = \dfrac{16}{30} = \dfrac{8}{15} \approx 0.5333$

Exercises for Example 1

Find tan D and tan E as fractions in simplified form and as decimals. Round to four decimal places if necessary.

1.
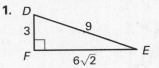

2.

3.
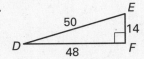

Geometry, Concepts and Skills
Practice Workbook with Examples

Reteaching with Practice

For use with pages 556–562

EXAMPLE 2 *Use a Calculator for Tangent*

Approximate tan 10° to four decimal places.

SOLUTION

Calculator keystrokes	Display	Rounded value
10 **TAN** or **TAN** 10 **ENTER**	0.1763269807	0.1763

Exercises for Example 2

Use a calculator to approximate the value to four decimal places.

4. tan 34°

5. tan 71°

6. tan 45°

7. tan 20°

EXAMPLE 3 *Find Leg Length*

Use a tangent ratio to find the value of x. Round your answer
to the nearest tenth.

SOLUTION

$$\tan 65° = \frac{\text{opposite leg}}{\text{adjacent leg}}$$ Write the tangent ratio.

$$\tan 65° = \frac{29}{x}$$ Substitute.

$$x \cdot \tan 65° = 29$$ Multiply each side by x.

$$x = \frac{29}{\tan 65°}$$ Divide each side by tan 65°.

$$x \approx \frac{29}{2.1445}$$ Use a calculator or table to approximate tan 65°.

$$x \approx 13.5$$ Simplify.

Reteaching with Practice

For use with pages 556–562

Exercises for Example 3

Find the value of x. Round your answer to the nearest tenth.

8.
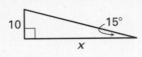

9.
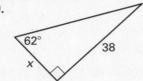

10.

EXAMPLE 4 *Find Leg Length*

Use two different tangent ratios to find the value of *x* to the
nearest tenth.

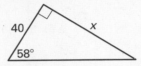

SOLUTION

First, find the measure of the other acute angle: $90° - 58° = 32°$.

Method 1

$$\tan 58° = \frac{x}{40}$$

$$40 \cdot \tan 58° = x$$

$$40(1.6003) = x$$

$$64.0 \approx x$$

Method 2

$$\tan 32° = \frac{40}{x}$$

$$x \cdot \tan 32° = 40$$

$$x = \frac{40}{\tan 32°}$$

$$x = \frac{40}{0.6249} \approx 64.0$$

Exercises for Example 4

**Write two equations you can use to find the value of x.
Then find the value of x to the nearest tenth.**

11.
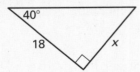

12.

13.
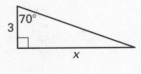

Geometry, Concepts and Skills
Practice Workbook with Examples

NAME_____ DATE _____

Reteaching with Practice

For use with pages 563–568

CALIFORNIA
Geometry Content Standards
18.0, 19.0

GOAL Find the sine and cosine of an acute angle.

VOCABULARY

For any acute angle in a right triangle, the ratio of the leg opposite the angle to the hypotenuse is the **sine** of the angle.

For any acute angle in a right triangle, the ratio of the leg adjacent to the angle to the hypotenuse is the **cosine** of the angle.

Sine Ratio: $\sin A = \dfrac{\text{leg opposite } \angle A}{\text{hypotenus e}}$

Cosine Ratio: $\cos A = \dfrac{\text{leg adjacent } \angle A}{\text{hypotenus e}}$

EXAMPLE 1 *Find Sine and Cosine Ratios*

Find sin *A* and cos *A*. Write your answers as fractions and as decimals rounded to four decimal places.

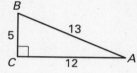

SOLUTION

$\sin A = \dfrac{\text{leg opposite } \angle A}{\text{hypotenus e}}$ Write ratio for sine.

$\sin A = \dfrac{5}{13}$ Substitute.

$\sin A \approx 0.3846$ Use a calculator.

$\cos A = \dfrac{\text{leg adjacent to } \angle A}{\text{hypotenuse}}$ Write ratio for cosine.

$\cos A = \dfrac{12}{13}$ Substitute.

$\cos A \approx 0.9231$ Use a calculator.

Exercises for Example 1

Find sin *A* and cos *A*. Write your answers as fractions and as decimals rounded to four decimal places.

1.

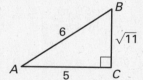

2.

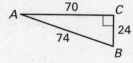

3.

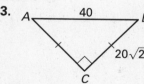

NAME _____ DATE _____

Reteaching with Practice

For use with pages 563–568

EXAMPLE 2 *Use a Calculator for Sine and Cosine*

Use a calculator to approximate sin 18° and cos 18°. Round your answers to four decimal places.

SOLUTION

Calculator keystrokes	Display	Rounded value
18 [SIN] or [SIN] 18 [ENTER]	0.309016994	0.3090
18 [COS] or [COS] 18 [ENTER]	0.951056516	0.9511

Exercises for Example 2

Use a calculator to approximate the value to four decimal places.

4. sin 33°   **5.** cos 33°   **6.** sin 8°   **7.** cos 67°

8. sin 85°   **9.** cos 13°   **10.** sin 0°   **11.** cos 0°

EXAMPLE 3 *Find Leg Lengths*

Find the length of the legs of the triangle.
Round your answers to the nearest tenth.

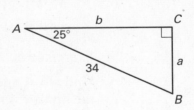

SOLUTION

$$\sin A = \frac{\text{leg opposite } \angle A}{\text{hypotenus e}} \qquad \cos A = \frac{\text{leg adjacent to } \angle A}{\text{hypotenuse}}$$

$$\sin 25° = \frac{a}{34} \qquad\qquad \cos 25° = \frac{b}{34}$$

$$34(\sin 25°) = a \qquad\qquad 34(\cos 25°) = b$$

$$34(0.4226) \approx a \qquad\qquad 34(0.9063) \approx b$$

$$14.4 \approx a \qquad\qquad\qquad 30.8 \approx b$$

Answer: In the triangle, *BC* is about 14.4 and *AC* is about 30.8.

Geometry, Concepts and Skills
Practice Workbook with Examples

NAME _____ DATE _____

Reteaching with Practice

For use with pages 563–568

Exercises for Example 3

Find the lengths of the legs of the triangle. Round your answers to the nearest tenth.

12.

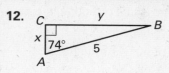

13.

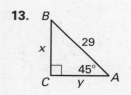

14.

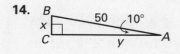

LESSON
10.6

NAME_____ DATE _____

Reteaching with Practice

For use with pages 569–575

CALIFORNIA
Geometry Content Standards
19.0

GOAL Solve a right triangle.

VOCABULARY

To **solve a right triangle** means to find the measures of both acute angles and the lengths of all three sides.

Inverse Tangent: For any acute angle A of a right triangle, if $\tan A = z$ then $\tan^{-1} z = m\angle A$.

Inverse Sine: For any acute angle A of a right triangle, if $\sin A = y$ then $\sin^{-1} y = m\angle A$.

Inverse Cosine: For any acute angle A of a right triangle, if $\cos A = x$ then $\cos^{-1} x = m\angle A$.

EXAMPLE 1 *Solve a Right Triangle*

Solve the right triangle. Round decimals to the nearest tenth.

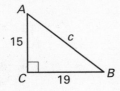

SOLUTION

To solve the triangle, you need to find c, $m\angle A$, and $m\angle B$.
To find c, use the Pythagorean Theorem.

$(\text{hypotenuse})^2 = (\text{leg})^2 + (\text{leg})^2$	Pythagorean Theorem
$c^2 = 15^2 + 19^2$	Substitute.
$c^2 = 586$	Simplify.
$c = \sqrt{586}$	Find the positive square root.
$c \approx 24.2$	Use a calculator to approximate.

To find $m\angle A$, use a calculator and the inverse tangent.

Since $\tan A = \dfrac{19}{15} \approx 1.2667$, $m\angle A \approx \tan^{-1} 1.2667$.

Expression	*Calculator keystrokes*	*Display*
$\tan^{-1} 1.2667$	1.2667 INV TAN or 2nd TAN 1.2667 ENTER	51.7105701

Because $\tan^{-1} 1.2667 \approx 51.7°$, $m\angle A \approx 51.7°$. To find $m\angle B$, use the fact that $\angle A$ and $\angle B$ are complementary. Since $\angle A$ and $\angle B$ are complementary, $m\angle B \approx 90° - 51.7° = 38.3°$.

NAME_____ DATE _____

Reteaching with Practice

For use with pages 569–575

Exercises for Example 1

Solve the right triangle. Round decimals to the nearest tenth.

1.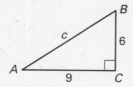

2.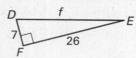

3.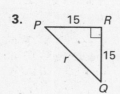

EXAMPLE 2 **Find the Measures of Acute Angles**

∠ A is an acute angle. Use a calculator to approximate the measure of
∠ A to the nearest tenth of a degree.

    a. $\sin A = 0.3112$ **b.** $\cos A = 0.4492$

SOLUTION

a. Since $\sin A = 0.3112$, $m\angle A = \sin^{-1} 0.3112$.

Expression	Calculator keystrokes	Display
$\sin^{-1} 0.3112$	0.3112 **INV** **SIN** or **2nd** **SIN** 0.3112 **ENTER**	18.1315629

Because $\sin^{-1} 0.3112 \approx 18.1°$, $m\angle A \approx 18.1°$.

b. Since $\cos A = 0.4492$, $m\angle A = \cos^{-1} 0.4492$.

Expression	Calculator keystrokes	Display
$\cos^{-1} 0.4492$	0.4992 **INV** **COS** or **2nd** **COS** 0.4492 **ENTER**	63.3076316

Because $\cos^{-1} 0.4492 \approx 63.3°$, $m\angle A \approx 63.3°$.

NAME _____ DATE _____

Reteaching with Practice

For use with pages 569–575

Exercises for Example 2

∠ **A is an acute angle. Use a calculator to approximate the measure of ∠ A to the nearest tenth of a degree.**

4. $\sin A = 0.9403$ **5.** $\cos A = 0.7844$ **6.** $\sin A = 0.2337$ **7.** $\cos A = 0.1818$

EXAMPLE 3 *Solve a Right Triangle*

Solve the right triangle. Round your answers to the nearest tenth.

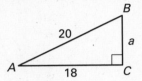

SOLUTION

To solve the triangle, you need to find a, $m\angle A$, and $m\angle B$.
To find a, use the Pythagorean Theorem.

$(\text{hypotenuse})^2 = (\text{leg})^2 + (\text{leg})^2$	Pythagorean Theorem
$20^2 = a^2 + 18^2$	Substitute.
$400 = a^2 + 324$	Simplify.
$76 = a^2$	Subtract 324 from each side.
$8.7 \approx a$	Find the positive square root.

Since $\cos A = \dfrac{18}{20} = 0.9$, $m\angle A = \cos^{-1} 0.9 \approx 25.8419328$, so $m\angle A \approx 25.8°$.

To find $m\angle B$, use the fact that $\angle A$ and $\angle B$ are complementary. Since $\angle A$ and $\angle B$ are complementary, $m\angle B \approx 90° - 25.8° = 64.2°$.

Exercises for Example 3

Solve the right triangle. Round your answers to the nearest tenth.

8. 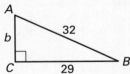   **9.** 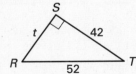   **10.**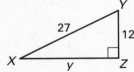

Geometry, Concepts and Skills
Practice Workbook with Examples

NAME_____ DATE _____

Reteaching with Practice

For use with pages 589–593

CALIFORNIA
Geometry Content Standards
21.0

GOAL Identify segments and lines related to circles.

VOCABULARY

A **chord** is a segment whose endpoints are points on a circle.

A **secant** is a line that intersects a circle in two points.

A **tangent** is a line in the plane of a circle that intersects the circle in exactly one point. The point is called a **point of tangency**.

EXAMPLE 1 *Name Special Segments, Lines, and Points*

In circle D at the right, name the term that best describes the given line, segment, or point.

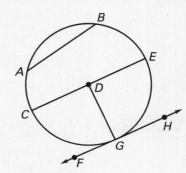

a. $\overline{AB}$

b. D

c. $\overline{CE}$

d. $\overline{DG}$

e. $\overleftrightarrow{FH}$

f. G

SOLUTION

a. $\overline{AB}$ is a chord because its endpoints are on the circle.

b. D is the center.

c. $\overline{CE}$ is a diameter because its endpoints are points on the circle and it passes through the center D.

d. $\overline{DG}$ is a radius because its endpoints are the center and a point on the circle.

e. $\overleftrightarrow{FH}$ is a tangent because it intersects the circle in exactly one point.

f. G is a point of tangency because it is the intersection point of a tangent and the circle.

NAME_____ DATE _____

Reteaching with Practice

For use with pages 589–593

Exercises for Example 1

Identify the term that best describes the given line, segment, or point.

1. $\overline{AF}$

2. $\overline{PF}$

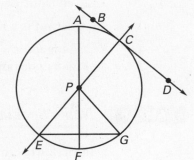

3. C

4. $\overleftrightarrow{BD}$

5. $\overline{EG}$

6. $\overline{PG}$

7. $\overleftrightarrow{CE}$

8. P

EXAMPLE 2 *Identify Special Segments, Lines, and Points*

In $\odot Q$ at the right, identify a chord, a diameter, two radii, a secant, two tangents, and two points of tangency.

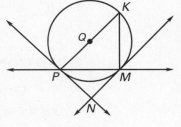

SOLUTION

$\overline{PM}$ is a chord. $\overline{KM}$ is also a chord. $\overline{PK}$ is a diameter.

$\overline{PQ}$ and $\overline{KQ}$ are radii. $\overleftrightarrow{PM}$ is a secant.

$\overrightarrow{NP}$ and $\overrightarrow{MN}$ are tangents. P and M are points of tangency.

Exercise for Example 2

9. In $\odot A$, identify the center, a chord, a secant, a diameter, a radius, a tangent, and a point of tangency.

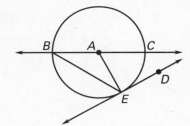

Geometry, Concepts and Skills
Practice Workbook with Examples

Reteaching with Practice

For use with pages 589–593

EXAMPLE 3 *Circles in Coordinate Geometry*

a. Name the coordinates of the center of $\odot P$.

b. What is the length of the radius of $\odot P$?

c. Line k is tangent to $\odot P$. Name the coordinates of the point of tangency.

d. Find the length of the chord $\overline{AB}$.

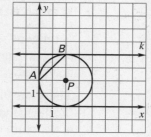

SOLUTION

a. The center of $\odot P$ is $P(2, 2)$.

b. The radius of $\odot P$ is 2.

c. The point of tangency is $B(2, 4)$.

d. To find the length of $\overline{AB}$, use the Distance Formula.

$$AB = \sqrt{(x_2 - x_1)^2 + (y_2 - y_1)^2} \qquad \text{Distance Formula}$$

$$AB = \sqrt{(2 - 0)^2 + (4 - 2)^2} \qquad \text{Substitute.}$$

$$AB = \sqrt{4 + 4} = \sqrt{8} = 2\sqrt{2} \qquad \text{Multiply and simplify.}$$

Exercises for Example 3

10. What are the coordinates of the center of $\odot A$? of $\odot B$?

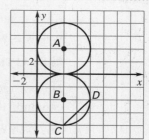

11. What is the length of the radius of $\odot A$?

What is the length of the diameter of $\odot B$?

12. What is the line that is tangent to both circles?

Name the point of tangency.

13. What is the length of chord $\overline{CD}$?

NAME _____ DATE _____

Reteaching with Practice

For use with pages 594–600

GOAL Use properties of a tangent to a circle.

VOCABULARY

A **tangent segment** is a segment that touches a circle at one of the segment's endpoints and lies in the line that is tangent to the circle at that point.

Theorem 11.1
If a line is tangent to a circle, then it is perpendicular to the radius drawn at the point of tangency.

Theorem 11.2
In a plane, if a line is perpendicular to a radius of a circle at its endpoint on the circle, then the line is tangent to the circle.

Theorem 11.3
If two segments from the same point outside a circle are tangent to the circle, then they are congruent.

EXAMPLE 1 *Using Properties of Tangents*

$\overleftrightarrow{EF}$ is tangent to $\odot D$ at point F. Find DE.
Round your answer to the nearest tenth.

SOLUTION

$\overline{DF}$ is a radius of $\odot D$, so you can apply Theorem 11.1 to conclude that $\overline{DF}$ and $\overleftrightarrow{EF}$ are perpendicular.

So, $\angle DFE$ is a right angle, and $\triangle DEF$ is a right triangle. To find DE, use the Pythagorean Theorem.

$(DE)^2 = (DF)^2 + (EF)^2$ Pythagorean Theorem

$(DE)^2 = 7^2 + 15^2$ Substitute 7 for DF and 15 for EF.

$(DE)^2 = 274$ Simplify.

$DE = \sqrt{274}$ Find positive square root.

$DE \approx 16.6$ Approximate with a calculator.

Reteaching with Practice
For use with pages 594–600

Exercises for Example 1

$\overleftrightarrow{MN}$ is tangent to $\odot P$. Find the value of *x*. Round your answer to the nearest tenth.

1.

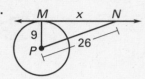

2.

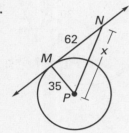

3.

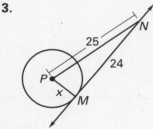

EXAMPLE 2 **Verify a Tangent to a Circle**

Tell whether $\overline{CD}$ is tangent to $\odot B$. Explain your reasoning.

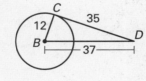

SOLUTION

Use the Converse of the Pythagorean Theorem to determine whether $\triangle BCD$ is a right triangle.

$(BD)^2 \stackrel{?}{=} (BC)^2 + (CD)^2$	Compare $(BD)^2$ with $(BC)^2 + (CD)^2$.
$37^2 \stackrel{?}{=} 12^2 + 35^2$	Substitute.
$1369 \stackrel{?}{=} 144 + 1225$	Multiply.
$1369 = 1369$	Simplify.

$\triangle BCD$ is a right triangle with right angle C. So, $\overline{CD}$ is perpendicular to $\overline{BC}$. By Theorem 11.2, $\overline{CD}$ is tangent to $\odot B$.

NAME_____ DATE _____

Reteaching with Practice

For use with pages 594–600

Exercises for Example 2

Tell whether $\overline{BC}$ is tangent to $\odot A$. Explain your reasoning.

4.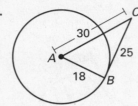

5.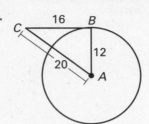

6.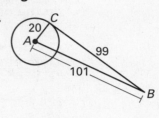

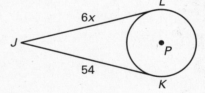

EXAMPLE 3 *Use Properties of Tangents*

$\overline{JL}$ is tangent to $\odot P$ at L. $\overline{JK}$ is tangent to $\odot P$ at K. Find the value of x.

SOLUTION

$JL = JK$ Two tangent segments from the same point are congruent.

$6x = 54$ Substitute $6x$ for JL and 54 for JK.

$x = 9$ Divide each side by 6.

Exercises for Example 3

$\overline{DE}$ and $\overline{DF}$ are tangent to $\odot C$. Find the value of x.

7.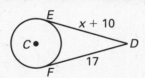

8.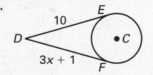

9.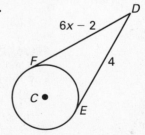

Reteaching with Practice

For use with pages 601–607

CALIFORNIA
Geometry Content Standards

21.0

GOAL **Use properties of arcs of circles.**

VOCABULARY

If the measure of $\angle ACB$ is less than 180°, then A, B, and all the points on $\odot C$ that lie in the interior of $\angle ACB$ form a **minor arc.** Points A, B, and all the points on $\odot C$ that do not lie on $\overset{\frown}{AB}$ form a **major arc.**

The **measure of a minor arc** is the measure of its central angle.

The **measure of a major arc** is the difference of 360° and the measure of the related minor arc.

A **semicircle** is an arc whose central angle measures 180°.

Two circles are **congruent circles** if they have the same radius.

Two arcs of the same circles or of congruent circles are **congruent arcs** if they have the same measure.

An **arc length** is a portion of the circumference of a circle.

Postulate 16   Arc Addition Postulate
The measure of an arc formed by two adjacent arcs is the sum of the measures of the two arcs.

Arc Length
In a circle, the ratio of the length of a given arc to the circumference is equal to the ratio of the measure of the arc to 360°.

EXAMPLE 1 *Identify and Find Measures of Arcs*

Identify the type of arc and then find its measure.

a. $\overset{\frown}{QS}$ **b.** $\overset{\frown}{QRS}$

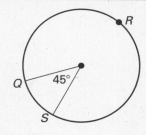

SOLUTION

a. $\overset{\frown}{QS}$ is a minor arc. Its measure is 45°.

b. $\overset{\frown}{QRS}$ is a major arc. Its measure is $360° - 45° = 315°$.

NAME_____ DATE _____

Reteaching with Practice

For use with pages 601–607

Exercises for Example 1

Identify the type of arc and then find its measure.

1. $\overset{\frown}{BCD}$

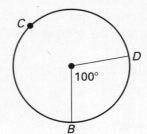

2. $\overset{\frown}{MN}$

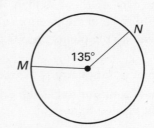

3. $\overset{\frown}{WXY}$

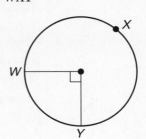

EXAMPLE 2 *Identify Congruent Arcs*

Are arcs $\overset{\frown}{AB}$ and $\overset{\frown}{CD}$ congruent?

a.

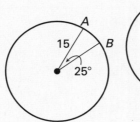

b.

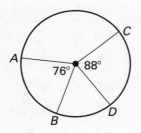

SOLUTION

a. Notice that $\overset{\frown}{AB}$ and $\overset{\frown}{CD}$ are in congruent circles since the radii are equal. Because $m\overset{\frown}{AB} = m\overset{\frown}{CD} = 25°$, $\overset{\frown}{AB} \cong \overset{\frown}{CD}$.

b. $\overset{\frown}{AB}$ and $\overset{\frown}{CD}$ are in the same circle, but $m\overset{\frown}{AB} \neq m\overset{\frown}{CD}$. So, the arcs are not congruent.

Geometry, Concepts and Skills
Practice Workbook with Examples

Reteaching with Practice

For use with pages 601–607

Exercises for Example 2

Are arcs *AB* and *CD* congruent? Explain your reasoning.

4.

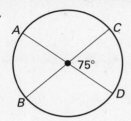

5.

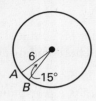 

EXAMPLE 3 *Find Arc Lengths*

Find the length of $\overset{\frown}{AB}$. Round your answer to the nearest hundredth.

SOLUTION

First, you need to know the measure of $\overset{\frown}{AB}$.

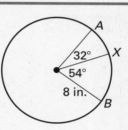

$m\overset{\frown}{AB} = m\overset{\frown}{AX} + m\overset{\frown}{XB}$ Arc Addition Postulate

$m\overset{\frown}{AB} = 32° + 54° = 86°$ Substitute and simplify.

Arc length of $\overset{\frown}{AB} = \dfrac{m\overset{\frown}{AB}}{360°} \cdot 2\pi r = \dfrac{86°}{360°} \cdot 2\pi(8) \approx 12.01$ inches

Exercises for Example 3

Find the length of $\overset{\frown}{AB}$. Round your answer to the nearest hundredth.

6.

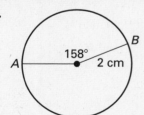

7.

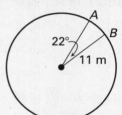

8.

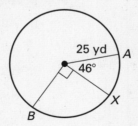

Reteaching with Practice

For use with pages 608–612

CALIFORNIA
Geometry Content Standards

21.0

GOAL **Use properties of chords of circles.**

VOCABULARY

Theorem 11.4
If a diameter of a circle is perpendicular to a chord, then the diameter bisects the chord and its arc.

Theorem 11.5
If one chord is a perpendicular bisector of another chord, then the first chord is a diameter.

Theorem 11.6
In the same circle, or in congruent circles, if two chords are congruent, then their corresponding minor arcs are congruent.
If two minor arcs are congruent, then their corresponding chords are congruent.

EXAMPLE 1 *Find the Length of a Segment*

In ⊙*P* the diameter $\overline{MN}$ is perpendicular to $\overline{AB}$.

a. Find the length of $\overline{AL}$.

b. Find the length of $\overline{AB}$.

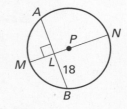

SOLUTION

a. Because $\overline{MN}$ is a diameter that is perpendicular to $\overline{AB}$,
you can use Theorem 11.4 to conclude that $\overline{MN}$ bisects $\overline{AB}$.
So, $AL = BL = 18$.

Answer: The length of $\overline{AL}$ is 18.

b. $AB = AL + BL$ Segment Addition Postulate

   $AB = 18 + 18$ Substitute 18 for AL and BL.

   $AB = 36$ Simplify.

Answer: The length of $\overline{AB}$ is 36.

NAME_____ DATE _____

Reteaching with Practice

For use with pages 608–612

Exercises for Example 1

$\overline{MN}$ is a diameter of $\odot P$. Find the length of $\overline{AB}$.

1.
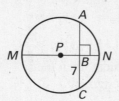

2.
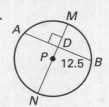

3.
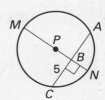

EXAMPLE 2 *Identify Diameters*

Determine whether $\overline{AB}$ is a diameter of the circle. Explain your reasoning.

a.
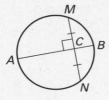

b.
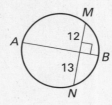

SOLUTION

a. Chord $\overline{AB}$ is a perpendicular bisector of chord $\overline{MN}$. By Theorem 11.5, $\overline{AB}$ is a diameter of the circle.

b. $\overline{AB}$ is *not* a diameter of the circle. Chord $\overline{AB}$ is perpendicular to chord $\overline{MN}$, but $\overline{AB}$ does not bisect $\overline{MN}$. You cannot use Theorem 11.5 to conclude that $\overline{AB}$ is a diameter.

Exercises for Example 2

Determine whether $\overline{AB}$ is a diameter of the circle. Explain your reasoning.

4.
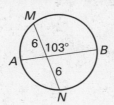

5.
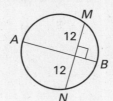

6.
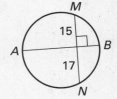

NAME_____ DATE _____

Reteaching with Practice

For use with pages 608–612

EXAMPLE 3 *Find the Measure of Angles and Chords*

Find the value of *x*.

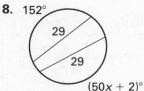

SOLUTION

Because $\angle APB \cong \angle CPD$, $\overarc{AB} \cong \overarc{CD}$. By Theorem 11.6, $\overline{AB} \cong \overline{CD}$.

$AB = CD$	If two minor arcs are congruent, then their corresponding chords are congruent.
$21 = 3x$	Substitute 21 for AB and $3x$ for CD.
$x = 7$	Divide each side by 3.

Exercises for Example 3
....

Find the value of *x*.

7.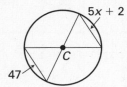

8.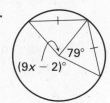

9.

Reteaching with Practice

For use with pages 613–619

GOAL Use properties of inscribed angles.

VOCABULARY

An **inscribed angle** is an angle whose vertex is on a circle and whose sides contain chords of the circle.

The arc that lies in the interior of an inscribed angle and has endpoints on the angle is called the **intercepted arc** of the angle.

If all the vertices of a polygon lie on a circle, the polygon is **inscribed** in the circle, and the circle is **circumscribed** about the polygon.

Theorem 11.7   Measure of an Inscribed Angle

If an angle is inscribed in a circle, then its measure is half the measure of its intercepted arc.

Theorem 11.8

If a triangle inscribed in a circle is a right triangle, then the hypotenuse is a diameter of the circle.

If a side of a triangle inscribed in a circle is a diameter of the circle, then the triangle is a right triangle.

Theorem 11.9

If a quadrilateral can be inscribed in a circle, then its opposite angles are supplementary. If the opposite angles of a quadrilateral are supplementary, then the quadrilateral can be inscribed in a circle.

EXAMPLE 1 *Find Measures of Inscribed Angles and Arcs*

Find the measure of the intercepted arc.

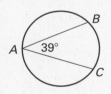

SOLUTION

$$m\angle BAC = \frac{1}{2}m\widehat{BC}$$ The measure of an inscribed angle is half the measure of its intercepted arc.

$$39° = \frac{1}{2}m\widehat{BC}$$ Substitute 39° for $m\angle BAC$.

$$78° = m\widehat{BC}$$ Multiply each side by 2.

NAME_____ DATE _____

Reteaching with Practice

For use with pages 613–619

Exercises for Example 1

Find the measure of the inscribed angle or the intercepted arc.

1.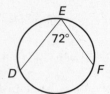

2.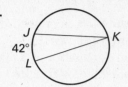

3.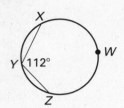

EXAMPLE 2
Find Angle Measures

P is the center of ⊙*P*. Find the values of *x* and *y*.

SOLUTION

Because △ *LMN* is inscribed in ⊙*P* and $\overline{LM}$ is a diameter, it
follows from Theorem 11.8 that △ *LMN* is a right triangle with
hypotenuse $\overline{LM}$. Therefore, $x = 90$. Because ∠*L* and ∠*M* are
acute angles of a right triangle, $y = 90 - 28 = 62$.

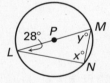

Exercises for Example 2

Find the values of *x* and *y* in ⊙*P*.

4.

5.

6.

Geometry, Concepts and Skills
Practice Workbook with Examples

NAME _____ DATE _____

Reteaching with Practice

For use with pages 613–619

EXAMPLE 3 *Find Angle Measures*

Find the values of x and y.

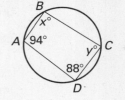

SOLUTION

Because $ABCD$ is inscribed in a circle, by Theorem 11.9 opposite angles must be supplementary.

$\angle B$ and $\angle D$ are opposite angles. $\angle A$ and $\angle C$ are opposite angles.

$m\angle B + m\angle D = 180°$ $m\angle A + m\angle C = 180°$

$x° + 88° = 180°$ $94° + y° = 180°$

$x = 92$ $y = 86$

Exercises for Example 3

Find the values of x and y.

7.

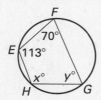

8.

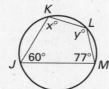

9.

NAME_____ DATE _____

Reteaching with Practice

For use with pages 620–626

CALIFORNIA
Geometry Content Standards
21.0

GOAL **Use properties of chords in a circle.**

VOCABULARY

Theorem 11.10
If two chords intersect inside a circle, then the measure of each angle
formed is one half the sum of the measures of the arcs intercepted by the
angle and its vertical angle.

Theorem 11.11
If two chords intersect inside a circle, then the product of the lengths of
the segments of one chord is equal to the product of the lengths of the
segments of the other chord.

EXAMPLE 1 *Find the Measure of an Angle*

Find the value of x.

SOLUTION

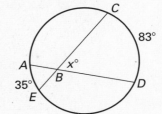

$\overline{AD}$ and $\overline{CE}$ are two chords that intersect inside the circle.
So, you can use Theorem 11.10.

$x° = \frac{1}{2}(m\widehat{AE} + m\widehat{CD})$ Use Theorem 11.10.

$x° = \frac{1}{2}(35° + 83°)$ Substitute 35° for $m\widehat{AE}$ and 83° for $m\widehat{CD}$.

$x = \frac{1}{2}(118)$ Add.

$x = 59$ Multiply.

Exercises for Example 1

Find the value of *x*.

1.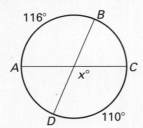

2.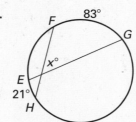

Geometry, Concepts and Skills
Practice Workbook with Examples

Reteaching with Practice

For use with pages 620–626

EXAMPLE 2 *Find the Measure of an Arc*

Find the value of x.

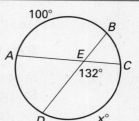

SOLUTION

$m\angle CED = \frac{1}{2}(m\widehat{AB} + m\widehat{CD})$ Use Theorem 11.10.

$132° = \frac{1}{2}(100° + x°)$ Substitute $132°$ for $m\angle CED$, $100°$ for $m\widehat{AB}$ and $x°$ for $m\widehat{CD}$.

$132 = 50 + \frac{1}{2}x$ Use the distributive property.

$82 = \frac{1}{2}x$ Subtract 50 from each side.

$164 = x$ Multiply each side by 2.

Exercises for Example 2

Find the value of **x**.

3.

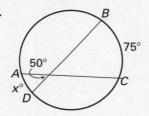

4.

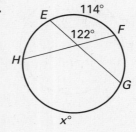

5.

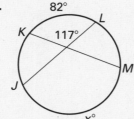

NAME _____   DATE _____

Reteaching with Practice

For use with pages 620–626

EXAMPLE 3 *Find Segment Lengths*

Find the value of x.

SOLUTION

Notice that $\overline{AC}$ and $\overline{BD}$ are chords that intersect at E.
So, you can use Theorem 11.11.

$AE \cdot CE = BE \cdot DE$	Use Theorem 11.11.
$3 \cdot x = 9 \cdot 4$	Substitute 3 for AE, x for CE, 9 for BE, and 4 for DE.
$3x = 36$	Multiply.
$x = 12$	Divide each side by 3.

Exercises for Example 3

Find the value of x.

6.

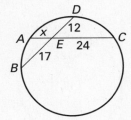

7.

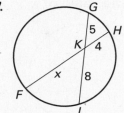

8.

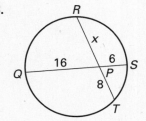

Geometry, Concepts and Skills
Practice Workbook with Examples

NAME _____ DATE _____

Reteaching with Practice

For use with pages 627–632

CALIFORNIA
Geometry Content Standards
16.0

GOAL Write and graph the equation of a circle.

VOCABULARY

$x^2 + y^2 = r^2$ is an equation of a circle with center at the origin and radius r.

Standard Equation of a Circle
In the coordinate plane, the standard equation of a circle with center (h, k) and radius r is $(x - h)^2 + (y - k)^2 = r^2$.

EXAMPLE 1 *Write an Equation of a Circle*

Write an equation of the circle.

SOLUTION

The radius is 7 and the center is at the origin.

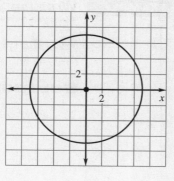

$x^2 + y^2 = r^2$ Write an equation of a circle with center at the origin.

$x^2 + y^2 = 7^2$ Substitute 7 for r.

$x^2 + y^2 = 49$ Simplify.

Answer: An equation of the circle is $x^2 + y^2 = 49$.

Exercises for Example 1

Write an equation of the circle.

1.

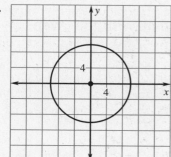

2.

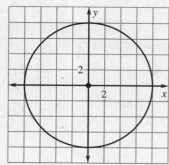

Reteaching with Practice

For use with pages 627–632

3.

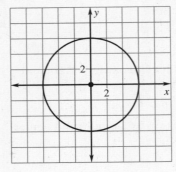

EXAMPLE 2 *Write the Standard Equation of a Circle*

Write the standard equation of the circle with center
$(-2, 4)$ and radius 5.

SOLUTION

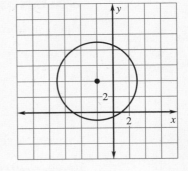

$(x - h)^2 + (y - k)^2 = r^2$ Write the standard
                                 equation of a circle.

$(x - (-2))^2 + (y - 4)^2 = 5^2$ Substitute -2 for h,
                                    4 for k, and 5 for r.

$(x + 2)^2 + (y - 4)^2 = 25$ Simplify.

Answer: The standard equation of the circle is $(x + 2)^2 + (y - 4)^2 = 25$.

Exercises for Example 2

**Write the standard equation of the circle with the given
center and radius.**

4. center $(1, 0)$, radius 3

5. center $(-2, -5)$, radius 9

6. center $(7, -1)$, radius 6

7. center $(-3, 8)$, radius 12

Geometry, Concepts and Skills
Practice Workbook with Examples

NAME _____ DATE _____

Reteaching with Practice

For use with pages 627–632

EXAMPLE 3 *Graph a Circle*

Graph the given equation of a circle.

a. $x^2 + (y - 3)^2 = 16$

b. $(x - 3)^2 + (y + 5)^2 = 1$

SOLUTION

a. Rewrite the equation of the circle as $(x - 0)^2 + (y - 3)^2 = 4^2$. The center is $(0, 3)$ and the radius is 4.

b. Rewrite the equation of the circle as $(x - 3)^2 + (y - (-5))^2 = 1^2$. The center is $(3, -5)$ and the radius is 1.

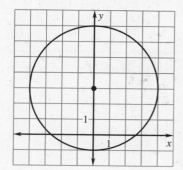
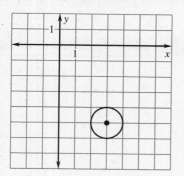

Exercises for Example 3

Graph the given equation of a circle.

8. $(x - 4)^2 + (y - 4)^2 = 9$

9. $(x + 3)^2 + (y - 1)^2 = 4$

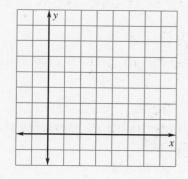
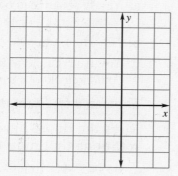

10. $(x - 2)^2 + y^2 = 16$

11. $x^2 + (y + 12)^2 = 9$

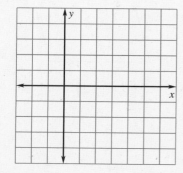
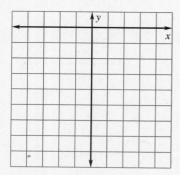

NAME _____ DATE _____

Reteaching with Practice

For use with pages 633–640

GOAL **Identify rotations and rotational symmetry.**

VOCABULARY

A **rotation** is a transformation in which a figure is turned about a fixed point.

The fixed point in a rotation is the **center of rotation**.

Rays drawn from the center of rotation to a point and its image form an angle called the **angle of rotation**.

A figure in a plane has **rotational symmetry** if the figure can be mapped onto itself by a rotation of 180° or less.

EXAMPLE 1 *Identify Rotational Symmetry*

Does the figure have rotational symmetry? If so, describe the rotations that map the figure onto itself.

a. Square

b.

c. Equilateral triangle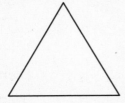

SOLUTION

a. Yes. A square can be mapped onto itself by a clockwise or counterclockwise rotation of 90° or 180°.

b. No. The figure does not have rotational symmetry.

c. Yes. An equilateral triangle can be mapped onto itself by a clockwise or counterclockwise rotation of 120°.

Exercises for Example 1

Does the figure have rotational symmetry? If so, describe the rotations that map the figure onto itself.

1. 45°–45°–90° triangle

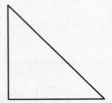

2. Rhombus

Geometry, Concepts and Skills
Practice Workbook with Examples

NAME_____ DATE _____

Reteaching with Practice

For use with pages 633–640

3. Hexagon

4.

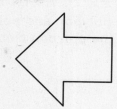

EXAMPLE 2 *Rotations*

Rotate *ABCD* 150° clockwise about point *P*.

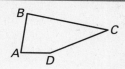

SOLUTION

1. To find the image of point *A*, draw $\overline{PA}$ and draw a 150° angle. Find *A'* so that *PA* = *PA'*.

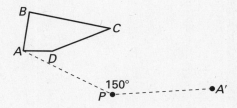

2. To find the image of point *B*, draw $\overline{PB}$ and draw a 150° angle. Find *B'* so that *PB* = *PB'*.

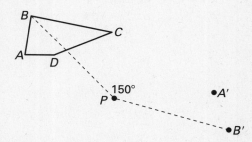

3. To find the image of point *C*, draw $\overline{PC}$ and draw a 150° angle. Find *C'* so that *PC* = *PC'*.

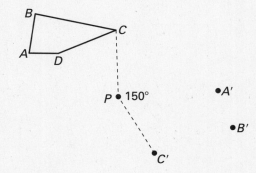

4. To find the image of point *D*, draw $\overline{PD}$ and draw a 150° angle. Find *D'* so that *PD* = *PD'*. Draw *A'B'C'D'*.

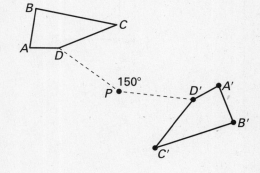

NAME_____ DATE _____

Reteaching with Practice

For use with pages 633–640

Exercises for Example 2

Trace the polygon and point *P* on paper. Use a straightedge and protractor to rotate the polygon clockwise the given number of degrees about *P*.

5. 140°

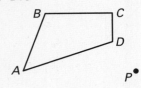

6. 90°

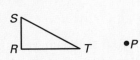

7. 135°

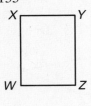

Directions: Circle the letter next to the correct answer. Give only one answer to each question. If you change an answer, be sure that the previous mark is erased completely.

Notes:
(1) Figures that accompany problems are drawn as accurately as possible EXCEPT when it is stated that a figure in not drawn to scale. All figures lie in a plane unless otherwise noted.
(2) All numbers used are real numbers. All algebraic expressions represent real numbers unless otherwise stated.

| LaTorry | 99 | 81 | 85 | 81 | 94 |
| Jose | 95 | 91 | 72 | 83 | 91 |

1. The chart above shows one quarter's test scores for two students. What is LaTorry's median test score?

   A 89

   B 85

   C 88

   D 81

2. Using only the data shown on the bar graph, which statement is valid?

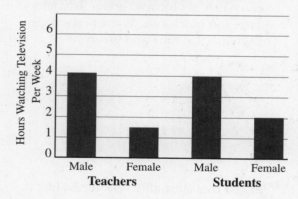

   A All males watch more television than all females.

   B Teachers watch more television than students.

   C On Thursday night, male teachers watched the most television.

   D Students watch more television than teachers.

3. When a 6-sided number cube is rolled twice, what is the probability of rolling both a one and a two?

   A 1:36

   B 1:18

   C 1:6

   D 35:36

4. What is the probability, expressed as a percentage, of rolling a 3 on the second roll, when one cube is rolled twice?

   A 1:6

   B 0.1667

   C 16.67%

   D 0.1667%

5. If $\frac{1}{36}$ is the probability of rolling two sixes, what is the probability of not rolling two sixes?

   A $\frac{1}{36}$

   B $\frac{1}{6}$

   C $\frac{5}{6}$

   D $\frac{35}{36}$

6. **Which of the following events is dependent?**

   A From a jar of 10 red and 10 white marbles, drawing a red on the second draw, without replacing the first marble.

   B Flipping a coin and getting heads on the third toss.

   C From a jar of 10 red and 10 white marbles, drawing a red on the second draw, after replacing the first marble.

   D When rolling two dice, rolling a six on the second die.

Item	Recycled in May
Newspaper	1.67×10^3 tons
Aluminum	1.5×10^3 tons
Glass	2.44×10^3 tons
Plastic	9.97×10^3 tons

7. **Put the items from the above chart in order from least to greatest amount recycled in May.**

   A aluminum, newspaper, glass, plastic

   B plastic, glass, newspaper, aluminum

   C plastic, glass, aluminum, newspaper

   D glass, aluminum, newspaper, plastic

8. $\frac{5}{12} \times \frac{6}{30} =$

   A $\frac{1}{12}$

   B $\frac{1}{6}$

   C $\frac{2}{5}$

   D $\frac{2}{9}$

9. $25.08 \div 12 =$

   A 0.445

   B 209

   C 2.08

   D 2.09

10. **Find the value of 3^5**

    A 15

    B 243

    C 125

    D 729

11. **What is $\frac{180}{250}$ expressed as a percentage?**

    A 72%

    B 18%

    C 45%

    D .72%

12. **In a 20 gallon fish tank, there are 9 yellow fish, 6 blue and green fish, and 15 silver and black fish. What percentage of the fish are blue and green?**

    A 18%

    B 20%

    C 25%

    D 50%

13. **A shirt that normally sells for $64.00 is on sale for $47.20. What is the percent of decrease?**

    A $16.80

    B 25%

    C 20%

    D 80%

14. You put $650 dollars into an account that has a simple interest rate of 16%. What will your balance be at the end of 3 years?

A $1014.58

B $754.00

C $962.00

D $1040.00

15. Anita's Department Store sells a leather purse for $78.50. Their cost on the purse is $37.25. Management decides to increase the retail price by 20%. What is the company's profit on the purse after the price increase?

A $25.55

B $49.50

C $56.95

D $94.20

16. Evaluate. Express the result in standard notation.

$$4^{-7} \times 4^4$$

A −64

B 64

C $\frac{1}{32}$

D $\frac{1}{64}$

17. Evaluate. Express the results in lowest terms.)

$$\frac{4}{5} - \frac{2}{15} + \frac{1}{6}$$

A $\frac{3}{4}$

B $\frac{25}{30}$

C $\frac{5}{6}$

D $\frac{29}{30}$

18. Evaluate the expression.

$$[(2^3)(2^{-5})][(3)(2)]^{-2}$$

A 2

B $\frac{1}{144}$

C 12

D −144

19. If the area of a square is 256 square units, how many units long is each side?

A 16

B 16.5

C 17

D 18

20. Evaluate the expression.

$$|-2.5|$$

A −2.5

B −2 2

C 2.5

D 2.5, −2.5

21. Seven times half the square of a number is equal to 56. Which of the following equations matches this statement?

A $\frac{[(7a)^2]}{2} = 56$

B $(\frac{7a}{2})^2 = 56$

C $\frac{(7^2a)}{2} = 56$

D $7(\frac{a^2}{2}) = 56$

22. Which of the following systems of equations best represents the following:

   Sarah is twice as old as one more than Juanita's age.

   Juanita is 7 years younger than Sarah.

   A $s = 2j + 1$
       $j = s - 7$

   B $2s = j + 1$
       $j = s - 7$

   C $s = 2(j + 1)$
       $j = s - 7$

   D $s = 2(j + 1)$
       $j - 7 = s$

23. Evaluate the expression for $x = 3$

   $$[(2 \cdot 3)^2 \div x] + 12$$

   A 16

   B 18

   C 20

   D 24

24. Which of the following graphs could represent the number of miles you have traveled as you drive at a steady rate?

   A    **B**

   C 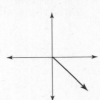   **D**

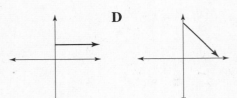

25. The graph below shows the amount of time it takes for the fire department to reach destinations at certain distances from the fire station. If you live 22 miles from the fire station, how long can you expect it to take the fire department to reach your home?

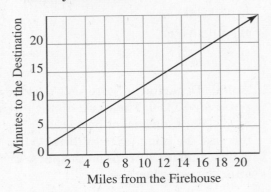

   Miles from the Firehouse

   A 20 minutes

   B 22 minutes

   C 25 minutes

   D 30 minutes

26. The rates for two cellular phone companies by the minute are shown on the graph below. How many minutes of time would you have to use for the two companies to charge the same amount?

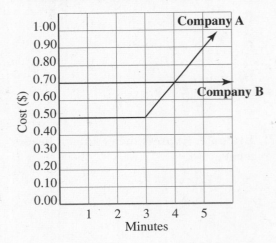

   A 3 minutes

   B 3.5 minutes

   C 4 minutes

   D 5 minutes

27. Evaluate the expression for $x = 3$

$$9 \cdot x^{-2} + 2$$

A -79

B -52

C 3

D 83

28. Evaluate the expression

$$\sqrt{(2x)(8x^3)}$$

A $16x^4$

B $4x^4$

C $4x^2$

D $4x$

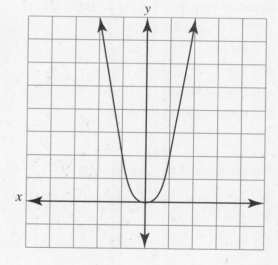

29. Which function is represented by the above graph?

A $y = 2x$

B $y = x^2$

C $y = 2x^2$

D $y = \frac{1}{2}x^2$

30. Which of the following graphs could represent $y = 2x$?

A 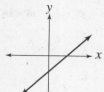   B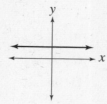

C 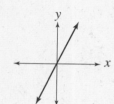   D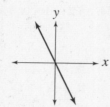

31. In the graph on the last problem, what should the slope of the line be?

A -2

B $-\frac{1}{2}$

C $\frac{1}{2}$

D 2

32. When plotting the following tables and fitting a line to the data, what rate will the slope represent?

Minutes	Meters
2	100
4	200
6	300

A 50 minutes per meter

B 50 meters per minute

C 100 minutes per meter

D 100 meters per minute

33. Solve for *m*.

$$6 - 5m \geq 21$$

A $m \geq -3$

B $m \leq -3$

C $m \geq 3$

D $m \leq 3$

34. Solve for *x*

$$\frac{5}{x} = \frac{6}{x} - \frac{1}{3}$$

A -3

B $-\frac{1}{3}$

C 3

D $\frac{1}{3}$

35. Which of the following is one solution for the given inequality?

$$(n - 2) \div (n + 3) > \frac{3}{8}$$

A -1

B 0

C 5

D 6

36. Two cars leave town at the same time going in the same direction, on the same road. One is traveling at 50 mph and the other at 30 mph. In how many hours will they 160 be miles apart?

A 8 hours

B 6 hours

C 4 hours

D 2 hours

37. The weight (*m*) of an object on Mars varies directly to its weight (*e*) on earth. A person who weighs 189 lb on earth weighs 42 lb on Mars. If a person weighs 37 lb on Mars, what would they weigh on Earth?

A 8 lb

B 148 lb

C 166.5 lb

D 185 lb

38. Sara left her house at 8:30 A.M. and arrived at her grandmothers for a picnic at 11:15 A.M. Her cousin Tim left his house at 9:45 P.M. and arrived at the picnic at 1:10 P.M. Their Uncle Manny didn't leave his house until 10:30 A.M., and he arrived at 1:50 P.M. Great-aunt Dorothy got picked up at 11:55 A.M., and arrived at 1:15 P.M. Which family member took the longest to get to the picnic?

A Sara

B Tim

C Uncle Manny

D Great-aunt Dorothy

39. 5 cups is equal to _____ quarts.

A 2.5

B 10

C 1.25

D 0.625

40. A house is 12m wide and 18m long. What are the dimensions of a model of the house that is built to a 300:1 scale?

A 4m wide, 6m long

B 4cm wide, 6cm long

C 36cm wide, 54cm long

D 36mm wide, 54mm long

41. A crate arrives with a volume of 2 ft³, and marbles packed at a density of 4 per in³. How many marbles are in the crate?

   A   576

   B   3456

   C   6,912

   D   13,824

42. If it takes you 75 minutes to drive to the beach at an average speed of 44 miles per hour. About how far do you live from the beach?

   A   66 miles

   B   60 miles

   C   55 miles

   D   50 miles

43. Find the area of the triangle

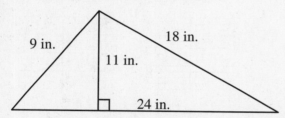

   A   280.5 in.²

   B   132 in.²

   C   108 in.²

   D   51 in.²

44. Find the circumference of the circle.

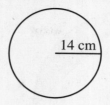

   A   88 cm

   B   92 cm

   C   108 cm

   D   616 cm

45. What is the volume of a box with a length of 16 inches, and a height and width of 8 inches?

   A   48 in.²

   B   128 in.²

   C   512 in.²

   D   1024 in.²

46. What is the area of the shaded region?

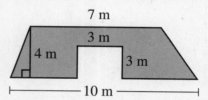

   A   21 m²

   B   25 m²

   C   28 m²

   D   36 m²

47. Find the area of the shaded region.

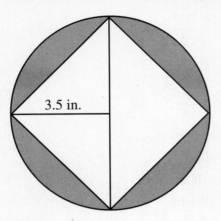

3.5 in.

A   24.5 in.²

B   20 in.²

C   14 in.²

D   12.5 in.²

48. Cube A has an edge of 2 units, cube B has an edge of 3 units.

What is $\frac{\text{Volume of Cube A}}{\text{Volume of Cube B}}$?

A $\frac{2}{3}$

B $\frac{1}{3}$

C $\frac{4}{9}$

D $\frac{2}{9}$

49. One cubic inch is approximately 16.38 cubic centimeters. Approximately how many cubic centimeters are there in 8 cubic inches?

A   81.9

B   131.04

C   168.2

D   204.75

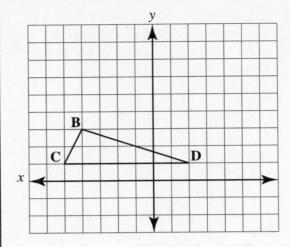

50. Which of the following triangles is the result of the translation $(x + 2, y - 1)$ on triangle BCD?

A   B

C 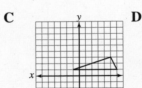   D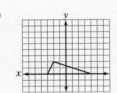

51. What is the area of the triangle formed by the points $(-2, 4)$, $(2, 1)$ and $(-2, 1)$?

A   4 square units

B   6 square units

C   8 square units

D   12 square units

52. Which of the following could NOT be the side lengths of a right triangle?

   A   3 cm, 4 cm, 5 cm

   B   6 in., 12 in., 14 in.

   C   7.5 ft., 18 ft., 19.5 ft.

   D   5 m, 12 m, 13 m

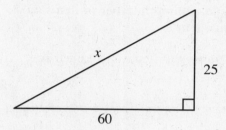

53. What is the value of x in the above triangle?

   A   65

   B   68

   C   72

   D   85

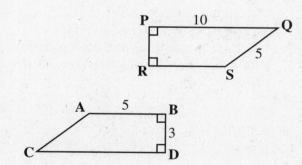

54. The above two figures are congruent. What is the measure of side CD?

   A   3

   B   5

   C   10

   D   15

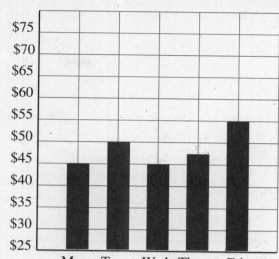

55. The above graph shows the amount of money Tina earned each day of the work week. Which day shows the greatest increase over the previous days earnings?

   A   Tuesday

   B   Wednesday

   C   Thursday

   D   Friday

56. What form of data display will best show each data value in organized intervals?

   A   box-and-whiskers plot

   B   bar graph

   C   stem-and-leaf plot

   D   scatter plot

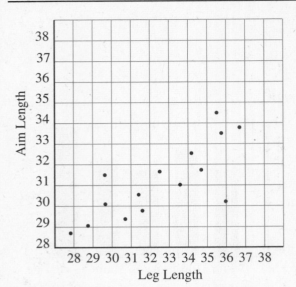

Aim Length / Leg Length

57. A group of college students measured their arm length from shoulder to wrist, and leg length from hip to ankle. Which of the following relationships is most likely to be supported by the above scatter plot?

    A There is no relationship between arm and leg length.

    B As leg length increases, arm length decreases

    C As leg length increases, arm length remains unchanged.

    D As leg length increases, arm length increases.

58. At an auction, six identical necklaces were sold at different times. The prices were $12 at 10 A.M., $28 at 12:30 P.M., $17 at 1 P.M., $25 at 11 A.M., $21 at 12 noon and $16 at 2 P.M. What relationship might be supported by the data given?

    A There is no relationship between selling price and time of day.

    B The selling price remains unchanged throughout the day.

    C The selling price increases as the time increases.

    D The selling price decreases as the time increases.

59. Amanda scored 97, 80, 85, 83, 72, 65, 79, 94 and 76 on nine quizzes. What is the lower quartile of the quiz scores?

    A 72

    B 74

    C 76

    D 80

60. Using the box and whiskers plot, what is the maximum number of items on a lunch tray?

Number of Items on a Lunch Tray

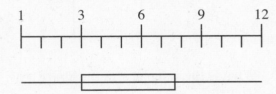

    A 3

    B 5

    C 7.5

    D 12

61. What other information is necessary to solve the problem?

> Kayla deposits $500 into a savings account. If she leaves it in the account for 3 years how much interest will it have earned?

    A What bank Kayla uses

    B The savings account number

    C The rate of interest

    D Kayla's hourly pay rate

62. Find the next term in the sequence 2, 3, 5, 9, 17...

A 27

B 30

C 33

D 35

63. Generally, a person's height as an adult can be found by taking the average height of their parents and adding 4 inches for a male, or subtracting 4 inches for a female. Which of the following equations would most likely represent a conjecture as to the adult height of a male child?

A $h = \dfrac{(f+m)}{2} - 4$

B $h = \dfrac{(f+m)}{2} + 4$

C $h = \dfrac{(f+m)}{4}$

D $h + 4 = \dfrac{(f+m)}{2}$

64. Sharon estimated by rounding to the nearest tenth, that (0.56)(0.7) should be close to 4.2. What should her estimate have been?

A 3.5

B 0.42

C 0.35

D 0.042

65. The graph below models Erica and Jan's drive to the mall. Using the graph to estimate, how much sooner should Erica arrive at the mall if they leave at the same time?

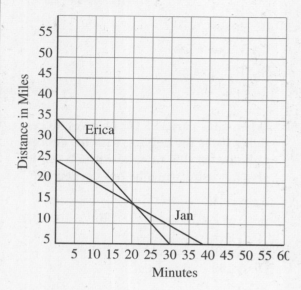

A 8 minutes

B 12 minutes

C 35 minutes

D 43 minutes

66. Jenna, William, and Ted each ate a take-out lunch today. They ordered beef tacos, a chicken salad and a vegetable pizza with extra onions. William doesn't eat meat, and Ted doesn't like salads. Who had each lunch?

A Jenna–pizza, William–salad, Ted–tacos

B Jenna–tacos, William–salad, Ted–pizza

C Jenna–salad, William–pizza, Ted–tacos

D Jenna–salad, William–tacos, Ted–pizza

67. Tina solved an equation to find the area of one of the tiles in her bathroom. Which of the following could be a reasonable solution?

A   1 foot

B   3 feet

C   1 square foot

D   100 square feet

68. When Luis earns \$5.00, he gives 40 cents to his sister for helping with his chores at home. At this rate, how much will he give his sister when he has earned \$75?

A   \$12.50

B   \$10.00

C   \$6.00

D   \$4.80

69. Simplify

$$\frac{\sqrt{16x^6}}{-(x^2)}$$

A -4

B $-4x$

C $-4x^2$

D $-8x^2$

70. Solve

$$-3|x| - 6 = -18$$

A   4

B   4, -4

C   8

D   8, -8

71. Which of the following has the same solution as

$$\frac{x}{4} - \frac{1}{3} \le \frac{5}{6}$$

A $4x - 3 \le 10$

B $x - 4 \le 5$

C $3x - 4 \ge 20$

D $3x - 4 \le 10$

72. Simplify

$$3y - 2 - (y-4)$$

A $2y + 2$

B $2y - 6$

C $4y - 6$

D $y + 2$

73. Alice's age added to 15 is equal to two years less than twice her age. How old is Alice?

A   13

B   15

C   17

D   19

74. Which of the following is the graph of $y = 2x + 1$?

A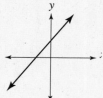

B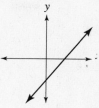

C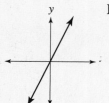

D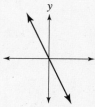

75. What is the *x*-intercept on the graph of the equation $2y = 3x - 6$?

A (2,0)

B (0,2)

C (3,0)

D (0,3)

76. Which of the following points lies on the line of the equation $x + 2y = 7$?

A (2,3)

B (0,-2)

C (7,1)

D (-1,4)

77. Which of the following could be the equation for a line that is parallel to $y = 2x + 5$?

A $y - 2 = 3x$

B $-6x + 3y = -9$

C $y = -2x$

D $2x = 2y + 5$

78. What is the solution for the system of equations?

$$2x + 3y = -1$$
$$3x + 5y = -2$$

A (0,-1)

B (1,-1)

C (-1,1)

D (-1, -1)

79. Factor

$$3x^2 - 27$$

A $3(x^2 - 9)$

B $(3x - 3)(x + 3)$

C $3(x + 3)(x - 3)$

D $3(x - 3)(x - 3)$

80. One solution is 28% sodium and is to be mixed with another containing 40% sodium to make 150 L of a solution containing 36% sodium. How much of each solution should be used?

A 100 L of 28% and 50 L of 40%

B 75 L of 28% and 75 L of 40%

C 60 L of 28% and 90 L of 40%

D 50 L of 28% and 100 L of 40%

Directions: Circle the letter next to the correct answer. Give only one answer to each question. If you change an answer, be sure that the previous mark is erased completely.

Notes:
(1) Figures that accompany problems are drawn as accurately as possible EXCEPT when it is stated that a figure in not drawn to scale. All figures lie in a plane unless otherwise noted.
(2) All numbers used are real numbers. All algebraic expressions represent real numbers unless otherwise stated.

1. At Washington High School, there are five 9th grade homerooms. The number of students in each room are 26, 18, 31, 31, and 29. What is the mean class size?

A 28

B 29

C 31

D 27

2. The scatter plot below compares the number of minutes that 20 students studied to the percentage of correct answers on a Social Studies exam. Which of the following statements is invalid?

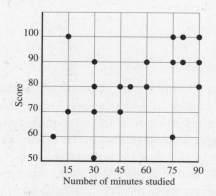

A Students may study for enough time, and still do poorly.

B Students may study very little, and still do well.

C The amount of time studied has little effect on how well students do on an exam.

D Most students scored between 70 and 90 percent

3. You flip three coins. What is the theoretical probability that exactly two land tails up?

A $\frac{3}{8}$

B $\frac{1}{4}$

C $\frac{1}{12}$

D $\frac{1}{2}$

4. Using the same coin toss, express the probability of the even of at least two heads as a decimal.

A 0.25

B 0.5

C 0.375

D 0.05

5. When P is the event of the shown spinner landing in the A section, what is 1–P?

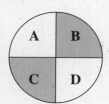

A $\frac{1}{4}$

B $-\frac{1}{4}$

C $\frac{3}{4}$

D $-\frac{3}{4}$

6. **Which of the following events is dependent?**

   A   Tossing a coin 4 times and getting a tail on the 3rd toss.

   B   From a jar of 10 red and 10 white marbles, drawing a red on the second draw, after replacing the first marble.

   C   From a jar of 10 red and 10 white marbles, drawing a white on the first draw.

   D   From a jar of 10 red and 10 white marbles, drawing a red on the second draw, without replacing the first marble.

7. $\dfrac{3}{8} \div \dfrac{3}{4} =$

   A $\dfrac{9}{24}$

   B $\dfrac{1}{8}$

   C $\dfrac{1}{2}$

   D   1

8. **Multiply. Round to the neared hundredth.**

   25.21 × 0.74

   A   18.66

   B   18.655

   C   186.55

   D   1.866

9. **Find the value of 2^8**

   A   16

   B   64

   C   128

   D   256

10. **Convert $\dfrac{3}{16}$ to a decimal.**

    A   5.3334   C   0.375

    B   0.1875   D   3.75

11. **A bag of jelly beans is made up of 0.17 white jelly beans, 0.22 pink jelly beans, 0.31 red jelly beans, 0.24 yellow jelly beans and 0.06 green jelly beans. What percentage of the jelly beans are red or yellow?**

    A   55%

    B   0.55%

    C   31%

    D   5.5%

12. **Last year Maria's flower garden produced 62 carnations and 94 roses. This year there were 94 carnations and 141 roses. What is the percent of increase in roses?**

    A   50%

    B   66.67%

    C   150%

    D   20%

13. **Terry found a pair of tennis shoes that he wanted at a local sports store. The original price was $80.00, but they were marked down to $54.00. He noticed that one of the shoes was discolored on the sole, and pointed it out to the manager. The manager offered him the shoes at an additional discount of 20% of the original price. How much did Terry pay?**

    A $ 38.00

    B $ 46.00

    C $ 43.20

    D $ 16.00

14. You deposit $800 in a savings account that pays 7.5% annual interest, compounded yearly. If you do not deposit any more money, what is the approximate account balance after 4 years?

   A   about $ 1040.00

   B   about $ 993.84

   C   about $ 1072.16

   D   about $ 1068.38

15. Evaluate and express the answer in standard notation.

   $$2^4 \times 2^{-8}$$

   A -8

   B -340

   C $\dfrac{1}{8}$

   D $\dfrac{1}{16}$

16. Evaluate and express the value in lowest terms.

   $$\dfrac{4}{5} - \dfrac{7}{10} + \dfrac{13}{20}$$

   A $\dfrac{2}{3}$

   B $\dfrac{17}{20}$

   C $\dfrac{3}{4}$

   D $\dfrac{15}{20}$

17. Evaluate the expression.

   $$(4^{-3} \cdot 4) \div 4^{-5}$$

   A $\dfrac{1}{4}$

   B   64

   C   4

   D $-\dfrac{1}{4}$

18. Between what two consecutive integers does $\sqrt{587}$ lie?

   A   79, 80   C   24, 25

   B   22, 23   D   80, 81

19. Solve the equation for a.

   $$a = |-4.75|$$

   A -4.75 C 4.75

   B $-4\dfrac{3}{4}$ D $-4.75, 4.75$

20. Which equation or inequality best represents the description:

   Four times the square root of a number is less than the same number divided by 5

   A $4\sqrt{n} = \dfrac{n}{5}$ C $4\sqrt{n} > \dfrac{n}{5}$

   B $4\sqrt{n} < \dfrac{n}{5}$ D $4n^2 < \dfrac{n}{5}$

21. Which system of equations best represents the following description.

   The number of tickets Nancy sold is equal to four times the number of tickets that Harry sold.

   The number of tickets that Harry sold is 16 less than the number of tickets that Nancy sold.

   A $n = 4h$
       $h = n - 16$

   B $4n = h$
       $h = n - 16$

   C $n = 4h$
       $h - 16 = n$

   D $4n = h$
       $h - 16 = n$

22. Evaluate the expression for $x = 5$

$$[10 + (x^2 \cdot 2)] \div 2$$

A 10

B 30

C 35

D 55

23. Phoebe makes ornamental wreaths from eucalyptus plants. The graph below is of the number of plants related to the number of wreaths Phoebe can make. How many wreaths can she make if she has 33 plants?

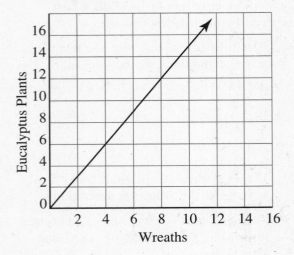

A 33

B 22

C 21

D 11

24. Which of the following graphs best represents the relationship of the amount of gasoline in your car as you drive down the road?

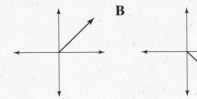

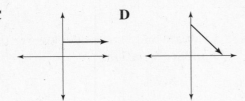

25. The following graph illustrates the weight of two friends. Complete the statement:

John weighs more than Olivia

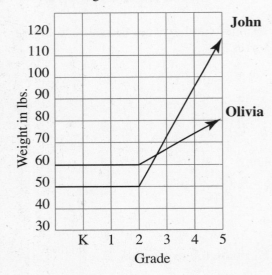

A at any given time.

B only in 3rd grade

C after 3rd grade

D before 3rd grade

26. **Evaluate the expression for** $x = 3$

$$(2x)^2 - 4 \cdot 2^{-2}$$

   A 35

   B 8

   C -8

   D -128

27. **Evaluate the expression**

$$\sqrt{(18x^3)(8x)}$$

   A $12x^2$

   B 12

   C 144

   D $36x^2$

28. **Which of the following graphs could be for the function** $y = -2x^2$

   A 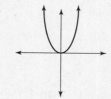   B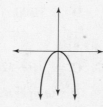

   C 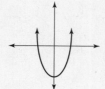   D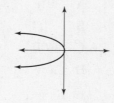

29. **What is the equation for the graph below?**

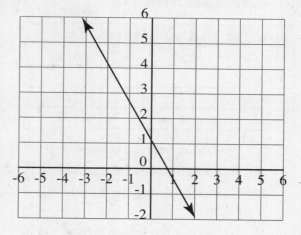

   A $y = -2x + 1$

   B $y = 2x + 1$

   C $y = -2x - 1$

   D $y = 2x - 1$

30. **The graph of a linear equation is through the ordered pairs (8, 6) and (4, –2). What is the slope of the line?**

   A -2

   B $-\dfrac{1}{2}$

   C $\dfrac{1}{2}$

   D 2

31. When plotting the following table on a graph, what would the slope of the resulting line represent?

Days Worked	Juans hours	Juans Pay
Monday	8	$66.00
Tuesday	5	$41.25
Thursday	4	$33.00
Saturday	6	$49.50

   A How many hours Juan worked

   B How much money Juan made

   C How many dollars per hour Juan makes

   D Whether or not Juan is a good worker

32. Solve for m:

$$14m + 3 \leq 15m + 7$$

   A $m \leq -4$

   B $m \geq -4$

   C $m \leq 4$

   D $m \geq 4$

33. Solve for x.

$$\frac{x+1}{3} - \frac{x-1}{2} = 1$$

   A 5

   B 1

   C –1

   D –5

34. Which of the following is a solution of the inequality $\left(\frac{8}{x}\right) - 4 > \left(\frac{2}{x}\right)$?

   A 1

   B $\frac{3}{2}$

   C 2

   D 3

35. Two cars leave town at the same time, going in opposite directions. One is traveling at 42 mph, the other at 60 mph. In how many hours will they be 255 miles apart?

   A 2

   B 2.5

   C 3.5

   D 4

36. A commissioned agent's income is a direct variation as to the value of policies sold per month. The agent made $4,200 on $80,000 worth of policies last month. How much will he make on $100,000 worth of policies?

   A $ 1,908

   B $ 5,000

   C $ 5,250

   D $ 5,300

37. $C = \frac{5}{9}(F - 32)$

The temperature outside is 30°C. What is the temperature in degrees Fahrenheit?

   A 30°F

   B −1°F

   C 86°F

   D 22°F

38. Put the following in order from smallest to largest:

12 yd^2

100 ft^2

14,976 in^2

   A 12 yd^2, 100 ft^2, 14,976 in^2

   B 14,976 in^2, 12 yd^2, 100 ft^2

   C 100 ft^2, 12 yd^2, 14,976 in^2

   D 100 ft^2 14,976 in^2, 12 yd^2

39. $C = \frac{5}{9}(F-32)$

The temperature in Seattle is 30°C. The temperature in San Diego is 89° Fahrenheit. Where is it warmer, and by how many degrees in Fahrenheit?

A   San Diego, 59°F

B   San Diego, 3°F

C   Seattle, 1°F

D   Seattle, 8°F

40. **Put the following in order from smallest to largest:**

6 yd²

13,824 in²

960 ft²

A   13,824 in², 6 yd², 960 ft²

B   13,824 in², 960 ft², 6 yd²

C   6 yd², 960 ft², 13,824 in²

D   960 ft², 6 yd², 13,824 in²

41. **A map of the library is drawn at a 48:1 scale. If the map has the check-out desk 2 inches from the door, how far is the door from the desk in the library?**

A   8 inches

B   24 inches

C   4 feet

D   8 feet

42. **Your job pays you $9.60 per hour. How much money would you make if you worked for 4 hours and 20 minutes?**

A $ 38.56

B $ 40.32

C $ 41.28

D $ 41.60

43. **The nearest water park is 88 miles from your house. If you drive at an average speed of 64 miles per hour, about how many minutes will it take you to get to the park?**

A   77.5 minutes

B   80 minutes

C   82.5 minutes

D   85 minutes

44.

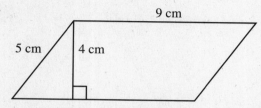

Find the area of the above parallelogram.

A   26 cm²

B   28 cm²

C   36 cm²

D   45 cm²

45.

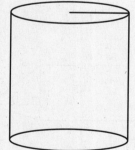

Find the volume of the cylinder when the radius is 1.5 inches, and the height is 7 inches

A   33 in²

B   41.5 in²

C   49.5 in²

D   66 in²

46. What is the perimeter of a 3 foot square?

   A 12 feet

   B 9 feet

   C 8 feet

   D 6 feet

47.

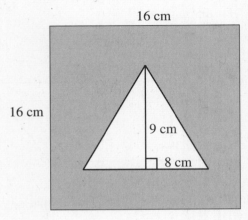

16 cm

16 cm

9 cm

8 cm

What is the area of the shaded portion of the figure?

   A 220 cm^2

   B 184 cm^2

   C 72 cm^2

   D 28 cm^2

48.

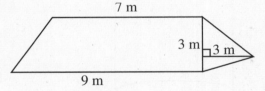

7 m

3 m 3 m

9 m

Find the area of the figure

   A 28.5 m^2

   B 39.5 m^2

   C 44 m^2

   D 67.5 m^2

49. A model of a playground is built at a 100:1 scale. If the model has an area of 64 in^2, what is the area of the playground, in square inches?

   A 6,400 in^2

   B 64,000 in^2

   C 640,000 in^2

   D 6,400,000 in^2

50. One cubic inch is approximately equal to 16.38 cubic centimeters. Approximately how many cubic inches are there in 819 cubic centimeters?

   A 500 cubic inches

   B 110 cubic inches

   C 55 cubic inches

   D 50 cubic inches

51.

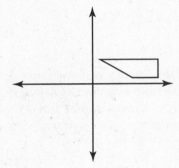

Which of the following is a reflection of the above parallelogram across the x-axis?

   A   **B**

   C   **D**

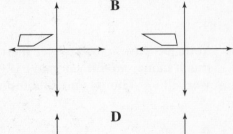

52. The points $(-1, 1)$, $(1,4)$, $(5,4)$, and $(3,1)$ are the vertices of a polygon. What type of polygon is formed by these points?

A   Square

B   Parallelogram

C   Trapezoid

D   Rectangle

53. Which of the following could be the side lengths of a right triangle?

A   5 cm, 9 cm, 7 cm

B   8 cm, 10 cm, 9 cm

C   5 cm, 12 cm, 13 cm

D   6 cm, 6 cm, 10 cm

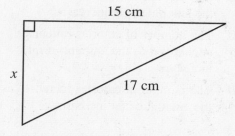

54. What is the value of x in the above triangle?

A   7 cm

B   8 cm

C   23 cm

D   64 cm

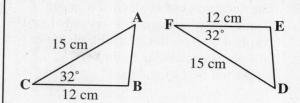

55. How are triangle *ABC* and triangle *DEF* related?

A   They are not related.

B   They are similar.

C   They are congruent.

D   Both are right triangles.

56. Which type of data display would be most useful to show the median and extremes of a data set?

A   stem-and-leaf plot

B   scatter plot

C   circle graph

D   box-and-whisker plot

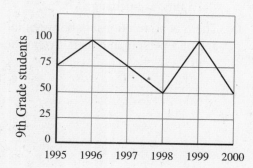

57. The above graph shows the number of ninth grade students attending Lincoln High School. Which year had the greatest decrease over the previous year?

A   1997

B   1998

C   1999

D   2000

58. The daily amount of sleep of a group of people of various ages was recorded and graphed on a scatter plot. Which of the following conclusions could be supported best by the data?

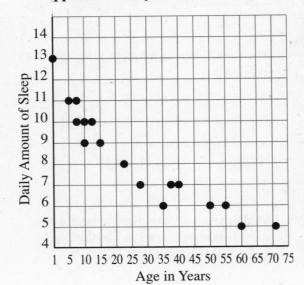

A As the age of a person increases, their sleep time increases.

B As the age of a person increases, their sleep time decreases.

C As the age of a person increases, their sleep time is unchanged.

D There is no relationship between the age of a person, and their sleep time.

59. The fat and calorie content of a 4 oz serving of different meat products is given in the table. What relationship exists between the fat and calorie content?

Meat Product	Fat Grams	Calories
Clams	1	81
Packaged Fish Protien	12	282
Tuna	8	191
Lean Beef	21	280
Ham, baked	9	180
Fried Chicken	14	199
Bologna, beef/pork mix	28	310

A There is no relationship between fat and calorie content.

B The number of calories decreases as the amount of fat increases.

C The number of calories remains unchanged as the amount of fat increases.

D The number of calories increases as the amount of fat increases.

60. Using the box-and-whiskers plot, what is the minimum number of hours spent reading at home?

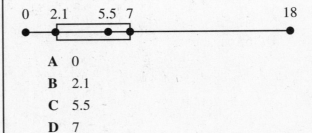

A 0

B 2.1

C 5.5

D 7

61. The scores of 12 students on a history exam are: 81, 82, 85, 65, 83, 82, 90, 97, 92, 70, 95 and 86. What is the upper quartile score?

A 84

B 85

C 91

D 97

62. Study the shape sequence below.

   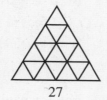

1   4   9   27

How many triangles that are one triangle units will be in the next term?

A 54

B 49

C 36

D 32

63.

> Over 72% of vehicle accidents in January in New York State are related to icy road conditions. Nationwide 12% of the vehicle accidents annually are related to icy road conditions. How does New York's annual percentage of vehicle accidents related to icy road conditions compare to the national average?

What additional information is required to solve the problem?

A The national number of vehicle accidents per year related to icy road conditions

B The annual percentage of vehicle accidents in New York state that are related to icy road conditions

C The number of vehicle accidents per year in New York state that are related to icy road conditions

D The total of vehicle accidents per year in New York state.

64. What mathematical conjecture, in the form of an expression, could represent the sequence which begins 0, 1, 3, 6, 10, 15, ...?

A $\dfrac{[n + (n-1)]}{2}$

B $n-1$

C $\dfrac{[(n)(n-1)]}{2}$

D $\dfrac{[(n)(n+1)]}{2}$

65. By rounding to the nearest whole number to estimate (17)(3.9), you know your exact answer should be:

A >88

B >78

C <68

D <65

66. Use the graph to estimate the time in minutes that it will take a fishing boat to travel 52 miles.

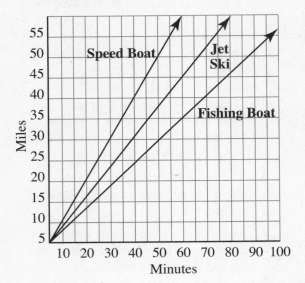

A 60 minutes

B 80 minutes

C 90 minutes

D 100 minutes

67. In one town, 1st Ave. is one-way going west, 2nd Ave. is one-way going east, 3rd Ave. is one-way going west, 4th Ave. is one-way going east and 5th Ave. is one-way going west. Using only this information, which of the following statements is a reasonable conjecture?

A Odd numbered avenues are one-way going east.

B Even numbered avenues are one-way going east.

C This town only has one-way streets.

D All of the streets in this town run either east or west.

68. The time it takes for a shotput to land after being thrown can be modeled by the equation $y = -5x^2 + 5$, where y is the distance the shotput is above ground level and x is the number of seconds from the throw. When $y = 0$, the shotput is on the ground. Without solving the equation, which of the following is a reasonable solution to how many seconds it will take the shotput to land after being thrown?

A −1 second

B 0 seconds

C 1 second

D 60 seconds

69. You are paid on an hourly basis, and in 8 hours you earn $56.00. How much will you have earned after you have worked 70 hours?

A $420   **C** $490

B $465   **D** $560

70. Simplify

$$\frac{(4x^3)^2}{(4x^2)^2}$$

A $4x^2$

B x^2

C x^5

D $4x^5$

71. Solve

$$3|b| - 4 = 2$$

A $2, -2$

B 2

C $\frac{2}{3}, -\frac{2}{3}$

D $\frac{2}{3}$

72. Which of the following has the same solution as

$$2(3x + 1) \leq 4(x - 4)$$

A $5x + 2 \leq 4x - 8$

B $6x + 1 \leq 4x - 4$

C $6x + 2 \geq 4x - 16$

D $6x + 2 \leq 4x - 16$

73. Simplify

$$3y - 2(4y - 5)$$

A $-5y + 10$

B $5y - 10$

C $5y + 10$

D $-5y + 5$

74. There are 4 more than twice as many girls in French class as there are boys. There are 22 girls, how many boys are there in French class?

A 18

B 13

C 9

D 6

75. Which of the following is the graph of the equation $y = -2x + 3$?

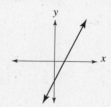

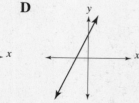

76. What is the y-intercept on the graph of the equation $8x + 2y = 24$?

A (0,3)

B (3,0)

C (0,12)

D (12,0)

77. For which line is the point $(2,-3)$ a solution?

A $y = x - 4$

B $2y = 2x - 1$

C $y = 3x + 1$

D $2x + 2y = -2$

78. Which of the following could be the equation for a line that is perpendicular to $2x + y = 7$?

A $y + 5 = 3x$

B $x + y = 2$

C $y = x - 14$

D $4y = 2x$

79. What is the solution for the system of equations?

$$m - n = 16$$

$$3m - 8n - 8 = 0$$

A (24,8)

B (16, 0)

C (8,8)

D (0,1)

80. One crew can do a job in 6 hours. If a second crew works with them, they can do the same job in 4 hours. How long would it take the second crew, if they were to do the job on their own?

    A 6 hours

    B 8 hours

    C 10 hours

    D 12 hour

CAHSEE
Practice Test 2

PRACTICE FOR LESSONS
ANSWER KEY

Lesson 1.1

1. After the first figure, one dot is being added to each of the top row and the bottom row of dots.

2. Larger and larger rings are being added to the figure. The rings are alternating in color between black and white.   **3.** Each number after the first is one less than the previous number.   **4.** Each number after the first is 3 times the previous number.

5.   **6.**   **7.** 48, 96

8. $-8, -11$

Lesson 1.2

1. odd   **2.** 10   **3.** Answers may vary. *Sample answer:* $-1 \times -1 = 1$ **4.** Answers may vary. *Sample answer:* 25

5. Answers may vary. *Sample answer:*

Lesson 1.3

1. The points in the figure are *A*, *B*, *C*, *D*, and *E*.

2. The lines in the figure are ℓ, *m*, and *n*.

3. The planes in the figure are *P* and *Q*.   **4.** *F*, *D*, and *B* are collinear.   **5.** Answers may vary. *Sample answer:* *A*, *B*, and *F*.   **6.** Answers may vary. *Sample answer:* *A*, *B*, *D*, and *F*.

7. Answers may vary. *Sample answer:* *A*, *B*, *C*, and *D*.   **8.** Lines ℓ and *m* are coplanar.

9. Answers may vary. *Sample answer:*

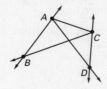

Lesson 1.4

1. *B*   **2.** *A*   **3.** The two lines do not appear to intersect.   **4.** *C*   **5.** *k*   **6.** ℓ **7.** *m*

8. Answers may vary. *Sample answer:*

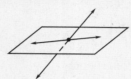

9. Answers may vary. *Sample answer:*

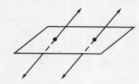

10. Answers may vary. *Sample answer:*

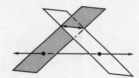

Lesson 1.5

1. $2\frac{3}{8}$ inches   **2.** $\frac{7}{8}$ inch   **3.** $JL = 18.5$

4. $BC = 4$

5. 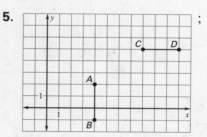 ;

the segments are congruent.

Lesson 1.5 *continued*

6.

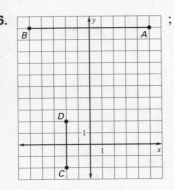

;

the segments are not congruent.

Lesson 1.6

1. $\angle EFG$ or $\angle GFE$ or $\angle F$ **2.** $\angle RTS$ or $\angle STR$, $\angle STU$ or $\angle UTS$, and $\angle RTU$ or $\angle UTR$

3. $32°$ **4.** $180°$ **5.** right **6.** acute

7. obtuse **8.** $110°$ **9.** $60°$

Lesson 2.1

1. $x = 7$ **2.** $x = 7$ **3.** $x = 2$ **4.** $x = 7.5$

5. $AM = 5, MB = 5$ **6.** $ML = 21, KL = 42$

7. $ST = 14, SM = 7$ **8.** $CM = 12.5$, $MD = 12.5$

9. $M(3, 5)$

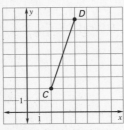

10. $M(-2, 1)$

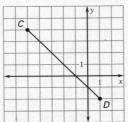

11. $M(2.5, -5)$

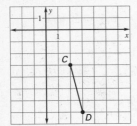

Lesson 2.2

1. $m\angle APS = 65°, m\angle SPB = 65°$

2. $m\angle CPS = 51°, m\angle DPS = 51°$

3. $m\angle EPS = 90°, m\angle SPF = 90°$

4. $m\angle GPS = 75°, m\angle HPS = 75°$

5. $m\angle CBD = 75°, m\angle ABC = 150°$; obtuse

6. $m\angle CBD = 90°, m\angle ABC = 180°$; straight

7. $x = 55$ **8.** $x = 25$ **9.** $x = 12.5$

Lesson 2.3

1. complementary **2.** supplementary

3. neither **4.** adjacent **5.** adjacent

6. nonadjacent **7.** $m\angle B = 79°$

8. $m\angle A = 58°$ **9.** $m\angle D = 2°$

Lesson 2.4

1. neither **2.** vertical angles **3.** linear pair

4. $x = 123$ **5.** $x = 88$ **6.** $x = 55$

7. $x = 126$ **8.** $x = 90$ **9.** $x = 9$ **10.** $x = 11$

Lesson 2.5

1. "It is raining outside" is the hypothesis. "There are clouds in the sky" is the conclusion.

2. "Two angles are vertical angles" is the hypothesis. "The two angles are congruent" is the conclusion. **3.** If a number is even, then it is divisible by two. **4.** If two angles are congruent, then the measures of the angles are equal.

5. Argument 2 is correct. The hypothesis (it is noon on Monday) is true, which implies that the conclusion (the children are in school) is true by the Law of Detachment. **6.** If I throw the stick, then my dog will bring it back to me.

Lesson 2.6

1. Transitive Property of Congruence

2. Symmetric Property of Congruence

3. Angle bisector; Angle bisector; Transitive, Congruence **4.** $x = 3$

Lesson 3.1

1. parallel **2.** perpendicular **3.** neither

4. perpendicular **5.** neither **6.** not skew

Geometry, Concepts and Skills
Practice for Lessons Answer Key

Lesson 3.1 *continued*

7. not skew **8.** skew **9.** plane *DEF*
10. $\overleftrightarrow{AC}$ **11.** $\overleftrightarrow{AB}$ **12.** $\overleftrightarrow{EF}$ or $\overleftrightarrow{DE}$ **13.** $\overleftrightarrow{DF}$

Lesson 3.2

1. Yes, enough information is given. $\angle 1$ and $\angle 2$ are both right angles. By Theorem 3.1, all right angles are congruent. **2.** Yes, enough information is given. $k \perp n$. By Theorem 3.2, $\angle 3$ is a right angle. By Theorem 3.1, all right angles are congruent. **3.** Yes, enough information is given. $k \perp \ell$. By Theorem 3.2, $\angle 4$ is a right angle. By Theorem 3.1, all right angles are congruent.

4. No, not enough information is given to conclude that $\angle 4 \cong \angle 5$. **5.** $\overleftrightarrow{GI}$ and $\overrightarrow{HJ}$ intersect and $\angle GPH \cong \angle HPI$. So, $\overleftrightarrow{GI} \perp \overrightarrow{HJ}$ (Theorem 3.3). By Theorem 3.2, $\angle GPJ$ is a right angle. **6.** $x = 9$ **7.** $y = 6$ **8.** $x = 7$

Lesson 3.3

1. alternate interior **2.** corresponding
3. alternate exterior **4.** same-side interior
5. $\angle 9$ and $\angle 13$, $\angle 12$ and $\angle 16$ **6.** $\angle 9$ and $\angle 11$, $\angle 10$ and $\angle 12$, $\angle 13$ and $\angle 15$, $\angle 14$ and $\angle 16$
7. $\angle 10$ and $\angle 11$, $\angle 14$ and $\angle 15$
8. $\angle 10$ and $\angle 14$, $\angle 11$ and $\angle 15$ **9.** alternate interior **10.** alternate exterior
11. corresponding **12.** same-side interior

Lesson 3.4

1. $m\angle 3 = 70°$ **2.** $m\angle 4 = 141°$
3. $m\angle 5 = 90°$ **4.** $m\angle 3 = 59°$
5. $m\angle 4 = 110°$ **6.** $m\angle 5 = 167°$
7. $m\angle 3 = 45°$ **8.** $m\angle 4 = 90°$
9. $m\angle 5 = 145°$ **10.** $x = 10$ **11.** $x = 49$

Lesson 3.5

1. *Converse:* If an angle is acute, then its measure is between 0° and 90°; the converse is true.

2. *Converse:* If $\angle 1 \cong \angle 2$, then $\angle 1$ and $\angle 2$ are vertical angles; the converse is false.

3. *Converse:* If line ℓ intersects plane P in a point and is perpendicular to every line in P that intersects it, then ℓ is perpendicular to P; the converse is true. **4.** No. You are not given enough information about the angles formed where r and t intersect. **5.** Yes. The two marked angles are corresponding and congruent. There is enough information to use the Corresponding Angles Converse to conclude that $r \parallel s$.

6. Yes. The angle congruence marks on the diagram allow you to conclude that $a \parallel b$ by the Alternate Interior Angles Converse Theorem.

7. No. Not enough information is given to conclude that $a \parallel b$.

Lesson 3.6

1.

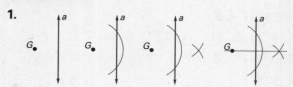

2.

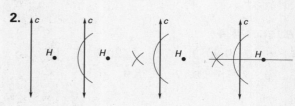

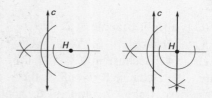

3. Using Theorem 3.11, since $a \parallel b$ and $b \parallel c$ you can conclude that $a \parallel c$ **4.** Because corresponding angles are $\cong$, $a \parallel b$. Using Theorem 3.11, because $a \parallel b$ and $b \parallel c$ you can conclude that $a \parallel c$. **5.** $x = 6$ **6.** $x = 25$

Lesson 3.7

1. No, this is not a translation. The image is a mirror image of the original figure. **2.** No, this is not a translation. The original figure is rotated.

3. Yes, this is a translation. **4.** Every point moves 3 units to the right and 4 units down.

5. Every point moves 5 units to the left and 2 units down.   **6.** $(x, y) \rightarrow (x + 7, y + 2)$

7. $(x, y) \rightarrow (x - 4, y - 4)$

Lesson 4.1

1. isosceles   **2.** equilateral   **3.** scalene
4. scalene   **5.** equiangular   **6.** obtuse
7. acute   **8.** $\overline{KL}$ **9.** $\overline{JL}$ **10.** $\overline{JK}$

Lesson 4.2

1. $140°$ **2.** $60°$ **3.** $90°$ **4.** $73°$ **5.** $25°$
6. $45°$ **7.** $19°$ **8.** $120°$ **9.** $110°$

Lesson 4.3

1. $45°$ **2.** $57°$ **3.** $22°$ **4.** $x = 7.5$
5. $x = 45$ **6.** $x = 4$ **7.** $x = 10$ **8.** $x = 3$
9. $x = 12$

Lesson 4.4

1. 26   **2.** 9.9   **3.** 16.6   **4.** 20.2   **5.** 8.4
6. 10   **7.** 7.1   **8.** 7   **9.** 8.9

Lesson 4.5

1. Yes, $\triangle ABC$ is a right triangle.   **2.** No, $\triangle ABC$ is not a right triangle.   **3.** Yes, $\triangle ABC$ is a right triangle.   **4.** Because $400 < 520$, the triangle is acute.   **5.** Because $841 > 521$, the triangle is obtuse.   **6.** right   **7.** obtuse   **8.** acute

Lesson 4.6

1.

2.

3.

4.

5. $AP = 40$; $PD = 20$ **6.** $HP = 24$; $PG = 12$
7. $KP = 66$; $PM = 33$ **8.** 12   **9.** 3   **10.** 36

Lesson 4.7

1. $\angle F$ is smallest, $\angle E$ is largest.   **2.** $\angle K$ is smallest, $\angle L$ is largest.   **3.** $\angle Z$ is smallest, $\angle Y$ is largest.   **4.** $\overline{DF}$ is longest, $\overline{DE}$ is shortest.
5. $\overline{KL}$ is longest, $\overline{JL}$ is shortest.   **6.** $\overline{YZ}$ is longest, $\overline{XY}$ is shortest.   **7.** These side lengths are not possible because $14 + 17 = 31$.
8. These side lengths are not possible because $4 + 7 < 15$.   **9.** These side lengths are possible because $9 + 17 > 23$.

Lesson 5.1

1. *Sample answer*:

Corresponding Angles

$\angle K \cong \angle Z$

$\angle J \cong \angle Y$

$\angle L \cong \angle X$

Corresponding Sides

$\overline{JL} \cong \overline{YX}$

$\overline{KL} \cong \overline{ZX}$

$\overline{JK} \cong \overline{YZ}$

Congruence Statement: $\triangle KJL \cong \triangle ZYX$

2. *Sample answer*:

Corresponding Angles

$\angle N \cong \angle Q$

$\angle M \cong \angle R$

$\angle P \cong \angle S$

Corresponding Sides

$\overline{NP} \cong \overline{QS}$

$\overline{MN} \cong \overline{RQ}$

$\overline{MP} \cong \overline{RS}$

Congruence Statement: $\triangle NMP \cong \triangle QRS$

3. $DE = 22$, $m\angle C = 90°$
4. $BC = 19$, $m\angle F = 65°$
5. *Sample answer*:

$\triangle EGF \cong \triangle HGF$

6. *Sample answer*:

$\triangle JKL \cong \triangle LMN$

Lesson 5.2

1. No; you know from the diagram that $\overline{AB} \cong \overline{DB}$. By the Reflexive Property, you also know that $\overline{BC} \cong \overline{BC}$. But you do not know if the corresponding third sides are congruent, so you cannot use the SSS Congruence Postulate.

2. Yes; you know from the diagram that $\overline{EF} \cong \overline{HI}$, $\overline{EG} \cong \overline{HG}$, and $\overline{FG} \cong \overline{IG}$. Because the corresponding sides are congruent, you can use the SSS Congruence Postulate to conclude that the triangles are congruent.

3. Yes; you know from the diagram that $\overline{FD} \cong \overline{LK}$, $\overline{DE} \cong \overline{KJ}$, and $\angle D \cong \angle K$. $\angle D$ is the angle included by $\overline{FD}$ and $\overline{DE}$ and $\angle K$ is the angle included by $\overline{LK}$ and $\overline{KJ}$. So, you can use the SAS Congruence Postulate to conclude that the triangles are congruent. **4.** No; you know from the diagram that $\overline{LM} \cong \overline{RP}$, $\overline{MN} \cong \overline{QR}$, and $\angle M \cong \angle P$. $\angle M$ is the angle included by $\overline{LM}$ and $\overline{MN}$, but $\angle P$ is not the angle included by $\overline{PR}$ and $\overline{QR}$. So, you cannot use the SAS Congruence Postulate.

5. 1. $\overline{WZ} \cong \overline{YZ}$

    2. Given

    3. $\angle WZX \cong \angle YZX$

    4. Reflexive Property of Congruence

    5. SAS Congruence Postulate

Lesson 5.3

1. You know that $\angle M \cong \angle R$ and $\overline{MP} \cong \overline{RP}$. $\angle MPN \cong \angle RPQ$ because they are vertical angles. $\overline{MP}$ is the side included by $\angle M$ and $\angle MPN$, and $\overline{RP}$ is the side included by $\angle R$ and $\angle RPQ$. So, you can use the ASA Congruence Postulate. **2.** You know that $\angle WXY \cong \angle Z$ and $\angle WYX \cong \angle YXZ$. $\overline{XY} \cong \overline{XY}$ by the Reflexive Property of Congruence. $\overline{XY}$ is the side included by $\angle WXY$ and $\angle WYX$, but $\overline{XY}$ is not the side included by $\angle Z$ and $\angle YXZ$. So, you cannot use the ASA Congruence Postulate. **3.** No; you need $\angle E \cong \angle G$ to use the AAS Congruence Theorem to show that $\triangle DEF \cong \triangle FGD$. **4.** yes

5. yes; ASA   **6.** yes; AAS   **7.** yes; AAS

Lesson 5.4

1. No, there is not enough information to use the HL Congruence Theorem because you do not know if $\triangle MNP$ is a right triangle. **2.** Yes; from the diagram, $\triangle QRS$ and $\triangle UTS$ are right triangles, and $\overline{QS} \cong \overline{US}$ (hypotenuse). Because $\overline{QS}$ bisects $\overline{RT}$, $\overline{RS} \cong \overline{ST}$ (leg). So you can use the HL Congruence Theorem to conclude $\triangle QRS \cong \triangle UTS$. **3.** yes; HL   **4.** yes; ASA

5. yes; AAS

6. 1. Given

    2. $\angle RST \cong \angle UST$

    3. Given

    4. $\overline{ST} \cong \overline{ST}$

    5. AAS Congruence Theorem

Lesson 5.5

1. 1. Given

    2. Definition of segment bisector

    3. $\overline{FJ} \parallel \overline{GK}$ and $\overline{JG} \parallel \overline{KH}$

    4. Corresponding Angles Postulate

    5. $\triangle FGJ \cong \triangle GHK$

    6. $\angle J \cong \angle K$

2. 1. Given

    2. $\angle BAC \cong \angle DAC$

    3. $\angle B \cong \angle D$

    4. Reflexive Property of Congruence

    5. AAS Congruence Theorem

    6. Corresponding parts of congruent triangles are congruent.

3.

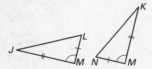

    1. Given

    2. $\overline{JM} \cong \overline{KM}$

    3. $\angle M \cong \angle M$

    4. SAS Congruence Postulate

Lesson 5.5 *continued*

4.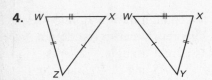

1. $\overline{WY} \cong \overline{XZ}$

2. Given

3. Reflexive Property of Congruence

4. $\triangle WXZ \cong \triangle XWY$

5. Corresponding parts of congruent triangles are congruent.

Lesson 5.6

1. $x = 11$ **2.** $x = 43$ **3.** $x = 6$ **4.** $x = 8$
5. $x = 13$ **6.** $x = \frac{1}{2}$ **7.** $x = 3; y = \frac{9}{2}$
8. $x = 3; y = 8$

Lesson 5.7

1. no **2.** yes; y-axis **3.** 1 **4.** 2 **5.** none

Lesson 6.1

1. Yes, the figure is a polygon with eight straight sides. **2.** Yes, the figure is a polygon with five straight sides. **3.** No, the figure is not a polygon because it has sides that are not segments.
4. Yes, the figure is a polygon with twelve straight sides. **5.** No, the figure is not a polygon because two of the sides intersect only one other side. **6.** The figure is a polygon with three sides, so it is a triangle. **7.** The figure is a polygon with six sides, so it is a hexagon. **8.** The figure is not a polygon because one of the sides is not a segment. **9.** $x = 65$ **10.** $x = 9$ **11.** $x = 6$

Lesson 6.2

1. $x = 12, y = 9$ **2.** $x = 23, y = 6$ **3.** $x = 1, y = 4$ **4.** $x = 9, y = 135$ **5.** $x = 55, y = 9$
6. $x = 12, y = 6$ **7.** $x = 7, y = 15$ **8.** $x = 1, y = 8$ **9.** $x = 5, y = 3$

Lesson 6.3

1. The quadrilateral is not a parallelogram. Both pairs of opposite sides are not congruent.

2. The quadrilateral is a parallelogram because both pairs of opposite sides are congruent.

3. The quadrilateral is not a parallelogram. Both pairs of opposite sides are not congruent.

4. The quadrilateral is a parallelogram, because both pairs of opposite angles are congruent.

5. The quadrilateral is not a parallelogram. Both pairs of opposite angles are not congruent.

6. The quadrilateral is a parallelogram, because both pairs of opposite angles are congruent.

7. *ABCD* is a parallelogram, because $\angle A$ is supplementary to $\angle B$ and $\angle D$.

8. The quadrilateral is not a parallelogram. The diagonals do not bisect each other. **9.** *JKLM* is not a parallelogram. $\angle K$ is supplementary to $\angle L$, but $\angle K$ is not supplementary to $\angle J$.

Lesson 6.4

1. $x = 7, y = 30$ **2.** $x = 2, y = 4$ **3.** $x = 3, y = 13$ **4.** $x = 18$ **5.** $x = 45$ **6.** $x = 8$
7. $x = 7$

Lesson 6.5

1. $m\angle E = 90°, m\angle F = 135°$ **2.** $m\angle F = 58°, m\angle H = 85°$ **3.** $m\angle E = 72°, m\angle G = 108°$
4. $x = 60, y = 40$ **5.** $x = 8, y = 15$
6. $AB = 14$ **7.** $AB = 11$ **8.** $AB = \frac{23}{2}$

Lesson 6.6

1. isosceles trapezoid **2.** parallelogram

3. trapezoid **4.** parallelogram **5.** square

6. rectangle **7.** Yes, *ABCD* is an isosceles trapezoid. Because same-side interior angles $\angle B$ and $\angle C$ are supplementary, you know that opposite sides $\overline{AB}$ and $\overline{CD}$ are parallel. Because same-side interior angles $\angle A$ and $\angle B$ are *not* supplementary, you know that $\overline{AD}$ and $\overline{BC}$ are *not* parallel. Therefore, you know that *ABCD* is a trapezoid since it has exactly one pair of opposite sides parallel. From the diagram you know that the legs $\overline{AD}$ and $\overline{BC}$ are congruent, so you know that *ABCD* is an isosceles trapezoid.

Lesson 6.6 *continued*

8. No, you cannot conclude that *EFGH* is a rhombus. Because $\angle F$ is supplementary to both of its consecutive angles, you know that *EFGH* is a parallelogram. From the diagram you know that two of the sides are congruent, but there is no information given about the other two sides.

9. Yes, *JKLM* is a parallelogram. By Theorem 6.9, because the diagonals bisect each other, *JKLM* is a parallelogram.

Lesson 7.1

1. $\frac{3}{14}$ **2.** $\frac{3}{1}$ **3.** $\frac{3}{4}$ **4.** $AB = 10, BC = 5$

5. $DE = 12, EF = 27$ **6.** $JK = 12, KL = 14$

7. $x = 1$ **8.** $y = 14$ **9.** $x = 23$

Lesson 7.2

1. $\angle L \cong \angle R, \angle M \cong \angle S$, and $\angle N \cong \angle T$;

$$\frac{RS}{LM} = \frac{ST}{MN} = \frac{RT}{LN};$$

$$\frac{RS}{LM} = \frac{12}{18} = \frac{2}{3}, \frac{ST}{MN} = \frac{16}{24} = \frac{2}{3},$$

and $\frac{RT}{LN} = \frac{20}{30} = \frac{2}{3}$

2. $\angle A \cong \angle E, \angle B \cong \angle F, \angle C \cong \angle G,$
and $\angle D \cong \angle H$;

$$\frac{EF}{AB} = \frac{FG}{BC} = \frac{GH}{CD} = \frac{EH}{AD};$$

$$\frac{EF}{AB} = \frac{9}{6} = \frac{3}{2}, \frac{FG}{BC} = \frac{6}{4} = \frac{3}{2},$$

$$\frac{GH}{CD} = \frac{9}{6} = \frac{3}{2}, \text{ and } \frac{EH}{AD} = \frac{12}{8} = \frac{3}{2}$$

3. $\triangle RST \sim \triangle XYZ, \frac{3}{2}$ **4.** $x = 10$ **5.** $x = 5$

Lesson 7.3

1. $\triangle ABC \sim \triangle EDF$ **2.** No, the triangles are not similar. **3.** $\triangle MNP \sim \triangle QRS$ **4.** No, the triangles are not similar. **5.** $\triangle JKN \sim \triangle LMN$; Because $\overline{KN} \perp \overline{JM}, m\angle JNK = m\angle MNL = 90°$. So $\angle JNK \cong \angle MNL$. From the diagram, you know that $\angle K \cong \angle M$. By the AA Similarity Postulate, you know that the triangles are similar.

6. $\triangle QRP \sim \triangle TRS$; Because $\overline{QP} \parallel \overline{ST}$, alternate interior angles $\angle Q$ and $\angle T$ are congruent. $\angle QRP$ and $\angle TRS$ are congruent because they are vertical angles. By the AA Similarity Postulate, the triangles are similar.

7. $\triangle PQR \sim \triangle WXV; x = 9$

8. $\triangle ABD \sim \triangle ECD; y = 4$

Lesson 7.4

1. The triangles are not similar.

2. $\triangle QRS \sim \triangle TWX, \frac{10}{9}$ **3.** $\triangle ABC \sim \triangle EFD$

4. $\triangle PQR \sim \triangle TSR$

5. $\angle F \cong \angle F$ by the Reflexive Property of Congruence.

$$\frac{FG}{FH} = \frac{1}{2} = \frac{FE}{FD}$$

The lengths of the sides that include $\angle F$ are proportional. By the SAS Similarity Theorem, $\triangle DFH \sim \triangle EFG$.

Lesson 7.5

1. $x = 5$ **2.** $y = 15$ **3.** No, $\overline{BE}$ is not parallel to $\overline{CD}$. The ratios of the two sides divided by $\overline{BE}$ are not equal. **4.** Yes, $\overline{BE}$ is parallel to $\overline{CD}$. The ratios of the two sides divided by $\overline{BE}$ are equal.

5. $x = 21$ **6.** $y = 12$ **7.** $x = 8$

Lesson 7.6

1. enlargement **2.** enlargement **3.** reduction

4. $\frac{7}{16}$ **5.** $\frac{19}{10}$ **6.** $x = 5$ **7.** $x = 16$

Lesson 8.1

1. convex **2.** concave **3.** convex

4. convex **5.** concave **6.** concave

7. Because the polygon is both equilateral and equiangular, it is regular. **8.** Although the polygon is equiangular, it is not equilateral. So, the polygon is not regular. **9.** Although the polygon is equilateral, it is not equiangular. So, the polygon is not regular. **10.** $x = 18$

11. $x = 5$ **12.** $x = 10$

Lesson 8.2

1. $360°$ **2.** $540°$ **3.** $1080°$ **4.** $69°$ **5.** $84°$
6. $167°$ **7.** $x = 70$. **8.** $x = 80$ **9.** $x = 19$

Lesson 8.3

1. 80 ft^2 **2.** 16 in.^2 **3.** 90 cm^2 **4.** $b = 3$ in.
5. $h = 9$ ft **6.** $h = 7$ cm **7.** 114 in.^2
8. 47 cm^2

Lesson 8.4

1. 30 in.^2 **2.** 72 cm^2 **3.** 14 ft^2 **4.** 130 cm^2
5. 27 in.^2 **6.** 35 ft^2 **7.** $h = 3$ in.
8. $b = 21$ cm **9.** $h = 2$ ft **10.** $\frac{3}{5}, \frac{9}{25}$

Lesson 8.5

1. 45 m^2 **2.** 204 cm^2 **3.** 196 ft^2 **4.** 120 yd^2
5. $b = 7$ m **6.** $h = 9$ ft **7.** $b = 11$ cm
8. 56 m^2 **9.** 70 in.^2 **10.** 72 ft^2

Lesson 8.6

1. 56 in.^2 **2.** 135 cm^2 **3.** 112 yd^2
4. $h = 3$ m **5.** $b_1 = 10$ ft **6.** $b_1 = 26$ yd
7. $h = 12$ units, $A = 306$ square units
8. $h = 24$ units, $A = 924$ square units

Lesson 8.7

1. 13 in. **2.** 69 cm **3.** 88 yd **4.** 907 in.^2
5. 79 cm^2 **6.** 3 m^2 **7.** 33 m^2 **8.** 43 cm^2
9. 7 ft^2

Lesson 9.1

1. no **2.** yes; hexagonal; hexagonal prism
3. yes; triangular; triangular prism
4. yes; trapezoidal; trapezoidal prism
5. square pyramid; five faces and eight edges; congruent faces: $\triangle AED \cong \triangle DEC \cong \triangle BEC \cong \triangle AEB$; congruent edges: $\overline{AB} \cong \overline{BC} \cong \overline{CD} \cong \overline{AD}$, $\overline{AE} \cong \overline{BE} \cong \overline{CE} \cong \overline{DE}$

6. square prism; 6 faces and 12 edges; congruent faces: $FGHJ \cong MLKN$ $FJNM \cong JHKN \cong HGLK \cong GFML$; congruent edges: $\overline{FG} \cong \overline{GH} \cong \overline{HJ} \cong \overline{FJ} \cong \overline{ML} \cong \overline{LK} \cong \overline{KN} \cong \overline{MN} \cong \overline{FM} \cong \overline{GL} \cong \overline{HK} \cong \overline{JN}$ **7.** 16 edges **8.** 12 vertices
9. 10 faces

Lesson 9.2

1.

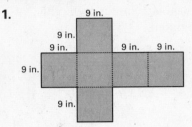

$S = 486 \text{ in.}^2$

2.

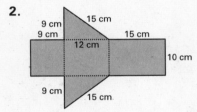

$S = 468 \text{ cm}^2$

3. 146 ft^2 **4.** 280 cm^2 **5.** 470 yd^2
6. 2004 m^2 **7.** 2827 ft^2 **8.** 251 in.^2

Lesson 9.3

1. 9 in. **2.** 12 in. **3.** 9 m **4.** 16 m^2
5. 317 m^2

Lesson 9.4

1. 72 yd^3 **2.** 960 ft^3 **3.** 210 m^3 **4.** 113 ft^3
5. 1335 cm^3 **6.** 4310 in.^3 **7.** 896 ft^3
8. 60 cm^3

Lesson 9.5

1. 324 yd^3 **2.** 32 m^3 **3.** 275 cm^3
4. 1257 ft^3 **5.** 75 m^3 **6.** 1078 cm^3
7. 89 m^3 **8.** 225 cm^3 **9.** 293 in.^3

Geometry, Concepts and Skills
Practice for Lessons Answer Key

Lesson 9.6

1. 2827 m^2 **2.** 5027 cm^2 **3.** 13 in.^{2}
4. 79 yd^2 **5.** 14,137 cm^3 **6.** 382 ft^3
7. 113 m^3 **8.** 3619 m^3 **9.** 348 yd^3
10. 7069 ft^3

Lesson 10.1

1. 3.7; $\sqrt{9} < \sqrt{14} < \sqrt{16}$, so $3 < 3.7 < 4$
2. 7.7; $\sqrt{49} < \sqrt{60} < \sqrt{64}$, so $7 < 7.7 < 8$
3. 4.8; $\sqrt{16} < \sqrt{23} < \sqrt{25}$, so $4 < 4.8 < 5$
4. 10.7; $\sqrt{100} < \sqrt{115} < \sqrt{121}$, so $10 < 10.7 < 11$
5. 8.5; $\sqrt{64} < \sqrt{72} < \sqrt{81}$, so $8 < 8.5 < 9$
6. 12.4; $\sqrt{144} < \sqrt{155} < \sqrt{169}$, so $12 < 12.4 < 13$
7. $x \approx 10.1$ **8.** $x = 6$ **9.** $x \approx 4.1$ **10.** 6
11. $\sqrt{330}$ **12.** $5\sqrt{6}$ **13.** $2\sqrt{6}$ **14.** $10\sqrt{5}$
15. $20\sqrt{5}$ **16.** 245 **17.** 144 **18.** 128

Lesson 10.2

1. $x = 30$ **2.** $x = 25\sqrt{2}$ **3.** $x = 2\sqrt{11}$
4. $x = 2$ **5.** $x = 11$ **6.** $x = 27$

7. The triangle is isosceles. By the Base Angles Theorem, its acute angles are congruent. The acute angles of a right triangle are complementary, so each acute angle must measure 45°; $x \approx 29.7$ **8.** The triangle is a 45°–45°–90° triangle by the same reasoning as in Exercise 7; $x \approx 50.9$ **9.** The triangle has a 90° angle and a 45° angle. By the Triangle Sum Theorem, the third angle must be 45°; $x \approx 13.4$

Lesson 10.3

1. $x = 30$ **2.** $x = 4$ **3.** $x = 100$ **4.** $x = 12.7$
5. $x = 18$ **6.** $x = 3$ **7.** $x = 30$; $y = 30\sqrt{3}$
8. $x = 1$; $y = \sqrt{3}$ **9.** $x = 13$; $y = 13\sqrt{3}$

Lesson 10.4

1. $\tan D = 2\sqrt{2} \approx 2.8284$
$\tan E = \dfrac{1}{2\sqrt{2}} \approx 0.3536$
2. $\tan D = \dfrac{4}{3} \approx 1.3333$
$\tan E = \dfrac{3}{4} = 0.75$

3. $\tan D = \dfrac{7}{24} \approx 0.2917$
$\tan E = \dfrac{24}{7} \approx 3.4286$
4. 0.6745 **5.** 2.9042 **6.** 1.0000 **7.** 0.3640
8. 37.3 **9.** 20.2 **10.** 73.7
11. $\tan 40° = \dfrac{x}{18}$, $\tan 50° = \dfrac{18}{x}$;
$x \approx 15.1$
12. $\tan 59° = \dfrac{84}{x}$, $\tan 31° = \dfrac{x}{84}$;
$x \approx 50.5$
13. $\tan 70° = \dfrac{x}{3}$, $\tan 20° = \dfrac{3}{x}$;
$x \approx 8.2$

Lesson 10.5

1. $\sin A = \dfrac{\sqrt{11}}{6} \approx 0.5528$
$\cos A = \dfrac{5}{6} \approx 0.8333$
2. $\sin A = \dfrac{12}{37} \approx 0.3243$
$\cos A = \dfrac{35}{37} \approx 0.9459$
3. $\sin A = \dfrac{\sqrt{2}}{2} \approx 0.7071$
$\cos A = \dfrac{\sqrt{2}}{2} \approx 0.7071$
4. 0.5446 **5.** 0.8387 **6.** 0.1392 **7.** 0.3907
8. 0.9962 **9.** 0.9744 **10.** 0.0000
11. 1.0000 **12.** $x \approx 1.4$, $y \approx 4.8$ **13.** $x \approx 20.5$, $y \approx 20.5$ **14.** $x \approx 8.7$, $y \approx 49.2$

Lesson 10.6

1. $c \approx 10.8$, $m\angle A \approx 33.7°$, $m\angle B \approx 56.3°$
2. $f \approx 26.9$, $m\angle D \approx 74.9°$, $m\angle E \approx 15.1°$
3. $r \approx 21.2$, $m\angle P = 45°$, $m\angle Q = 45°$
4. 70.1° **5.** 38.3° **6.** 13.5° **7.** 79.5°
8. $b \approx 13.5$, $m\angle A \approx 65.0°$, $m\angle B \approx 25.0°$
9. $t \approx 30.7$, $m\angle R \approx 53.9°$, $m\angle T \approx 36.1°$
10. $y \approx 24.2$, $m\angle X \approx 26.4°$, $m\angle Y \approx 63.6°$

Lesson 11.1

1. diameter **2.** radius **3.** point of tangency
4. tangent **5.** chord **6.** radius **7.** secant

Geometry, Concepts and Skills
Practice for Lessons Answer Key

Lesson 11.1 *continued*

8. center

9. The center of the circle is *A*.

$\overline{BE}$ is a chord.

$\overleftrightarrow{BC}$ is a secant.

$\overline{BC}$ is a diameter.

$\overline{AB}$, $\overline{AC}$, and $\overline{AE}$ are radii.

$\overleftrightarrow{DE}$ is a tangent.

E is a point of tangency.

10. ⊙*A*: *A*(4, 4), ⊙*B*: *B*(4, −4) **11.** The radius of ⊙*A* is 4. The diameter of ⊙*B* is 8. **12.** The *x*-axis is tangent to both circles. The point of tangency is (4, 0). **13.** $4\sqrt{2}$

Lesson 11.2

1. $x \approx 24.4$ **2.** $x \approx 71.2$ **3.** $x = 7$ **4.** $\overline{BC}$ is *not* tangent to ⊙*A* because △ *ABC* is *not* a right triangle. **5.** $\overline{BC}$ is tangent to ⊙*A* because △ *ABC* is a right triangle. **6.** $\overline{BC}$ is tangent to ⊙*A* because △ *ABC* is a right triangle. **7.** $x = 7$

8. $x = 3$ **9.** $x = 1$

Lesson 11.3

1. $\overparen{BCD}$ is a major arc. Its measure is 260°.

2. $\overparen{MN}$ is a minor arc. Its measure is 135°.

3. $\overparen{WXY}$ is a major arc. Its measure is 270°.

4. Yes, $\overparen{AB} \cong \overparen{CD}$ since $\overparen{AB}$ and $\overparen{CD}$ are in the same circle and $m\overparen{AB} = m\overparen{CD} = 75°$. **5.** No, $\overparen{AB}$ and $\overparen{CD}$ are not congruent. The arcs are not in the same circle or in congruent circles. **6.** 5.52 cm

7. 4.22 m **8.** 59.34 yd

Lesson 11.4

1. 7 **2.** 25 **3.** 5 **4.** $\overline{AB}$ is not a diameter of the circle. $\overline{AB}$ does bisect $\overline{MN}$, but $\overline{AB}$ is not perpendicular to $\overline{MN}$. **5.** $\overline{AB}$ is a diameter of the circle. $\overline{AB}$ is a perpendicular bisector of $\overline{MN}$.

6. $\overline{AB}$ is not a diameter of the circle. $\overline{AB}$ is perpendicular to $\overline{MN}$, but $\overline{AB}$ does not bisect $\overline{MN}$.

7. $x = 9$ **8.** $x = 3$ **9.** $x = 9$

Lesson 11.5

1. $m\overparen{DF} = 144°$ **2.** $m\angle JKL = 21°$
3. $m\overparen{XWZ} = 224°$ **4.** $x = 90, y = 38$
5. $x = 90, y = 10$ **6.** $x = 30, y = 90$
7. $x = 110, y = 67$ **8.** $x = 103, y = 120$
9. $x = 99, y = 90$

Lesson 11.6

1. $x = 113$ **2.** $x = 52$ **3.** $x = 25$
4. $x = 130$ **5.** $x = 152$ **6.** $x = 8.5$
7. $x = 10$ **8.** $x = 12$

Lesson 11.7

1. $x^2 + y^2 = 100$ **2.** $x^2 + y^2 = 64$
3. $x^2 + y^2 = 36$ **4.** $(x - 1)^2 + y^2 = 9$
5. $(x + 2)^2 + (y + 5)^2 = 81$
6. $(x - 7)^2 + (y + 1)^2 = 36$
7. $(x + 3)^2 + (y - 8)^2 = 144$

8.
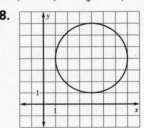

9.
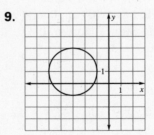

10.
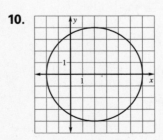

Geometry, Concepts and Skills
Practice for Lessons Answer Key

Lesson 11.7 *continued*

11.

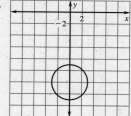

Lesson 11.8

1. No. The figure does not have rotational symmetry. **2.** Yes. A rhombus can be mapped onto itself by a clockwise or counterclockwise rotation of 180° about its center. **3.** Yes. The hexagon can be mapped onto itself by a clockwise or counterclockwise rotation of 180° about its center. **4.** No. The figure does not have rotational symmetry.

5.

6.

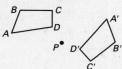

7.

CAHSEE
PRACTICE TEST
ANSWERS

Answers

Practice Test 1

Number	Answer	Correlation
1	B	6.1.1
2	A	6.25
3	A	6.31
4	C	6.3.3
5	D	6.3.3
6	A	6.3.5
7	A	7.1.1
8	D	7.1.2
9	D	7.1.2
10	B	7.1.2
11	A	7.1.3
12	B	7.1.3
13	B	7.1.6
14	C	7.1.7
15	C	7.1.7
16	D	7.2.1
17	C	7.2.2
18	B	7.2.3
19	A	7.2.4
20	C	7.2.5
21	D	7.1.1
22	C	7.1.1
23	D	7.1.2
24	A	7.1.5
25	C	7.1.5
26	C	7.1.5
27	C	7.2.1
28	C	7.2.2
29	C	7.3.1
30	C	7.3.3
31	D	7.3.3
32	B	7.3.4
33	B	7.4.1
34	C	7.4.1
35	D	7.4.1
36	A	7.4.2
37	C	7.4.2
38	B	7.1.1
39	C	7.1.1
40	B	7.1.2

256

CAHSEE
Practice Test Answer Key

41	D	7.1.3		65	A	7.2.3
42	C	7.1.3		66	C	7.2.4
43	B	7.2.1		67	C	7.3.1
44	A	7.2.1		68	C	7.3.3
45	D	7.2.1		69	B	Alg. 1, 2.0
46	B	7.2.2		70	B	Alg. 1,3.0
47	C	7.2.2		71	D	Alg. 1, 4.0
48	D	7.2.3		72	A	Alg. 1, 4.0
49	B	7.2.4		73	C	Alg. 1, 5.0
50	D	7.3.2		74	A	Alg. 1, 6.0
51	B	7.3.2		75	A	Alg. 1, 6.0
52	B	7.3.3		76	D	Alg. 1, 7.0
53	A	7.3.3		77	B	Alg. 1, 8.0
54	C	7.3.4		78	B	Alg. 1, 9.0
55	D	7.1.1		79	C	Alg. 1, 10.0
56	C	7.1.1		80	D	Alg. 1, 15.0
57	D	7.1.2				
58	A	7.1.2				
59	B	7.1.3				
60	D	7.1.3				
61	C	7.1.1				
62	C	7.1.1				
63	B	7.1.2				
64	B	7:2.1				

Practice Test 2

Number	Answer	Correlation
1	D	6.1.1
2	C	6.2.5
3	A	6.3.1
4	B	6.3.3
5	C	6.3.3
6	D	6.3.5
7	C	7.1.2
8	A	7.1.2
9	D	7.1.2
10	B	7.1.3
11	A	7.1.3
12	A	7.1.6
13	A	7.1.7
14	D	7.1.7
15	D	7.2.1
16	C	7.2.2
17	B	7.2.3
18	C	7.2.4
19	C	7.2.5
20	B	7.1.1
21	A	7.1.2
22	B	7.1.5
23	B	7.1.5
24	D	7.1.5
25	C	7.2.1
26	A	7.2.2
27	A	7.3.1
28	B	7.3.3
29	A	7.3.3
30	D	7.3.4
31	C	7.4.1
32	B	7.4.1
33	C	7.4.1
34	A	7.4.2
35	B	7.4.2
36	C	7.4.2
37	C	7.1.1
38	D	7.1.1
39	B	7.1.1
40	A	7.1.1
41	D	7.1.2
42	D	7.1.3
43	C	7.1.3
44	C	7.2.1
45	C	7.2.1
46	A	7.2.1
47	A	7.2.2

CAHSEE
Practice Test Answer Key

48	B	7.2.2	72	D	Alg. 1, 4.0
49	C	7.2.3	73	A	Alg. 1, 4.0
50	D	7.2.4	74	C	Alg. 1, 5.0
51	A	7.3.2	75	B	Alg. 1, 6.0
52	B	7.3.2	76	C	Alg. 1, 6.0
53	C	7.3.3	77	D	Alg. 1, 7.0
54	B	7.3.3	78	D	Alg. 1, 8.0
55	C	7.3.4	79	A	Alg. 1, 9.0
56	D	7.1.1	80	C	Alg. 1, 10.0
57	D	7.1.1	81	D	Alg. 1, 15.0
58	B	7.1.2			
59	D	7.1.2			
60	A	7.1.3			
61	C	7.1.3			
62	C	7.1.1			
63	B	7.1.1			
64	C	7.1.2			
65	C	7.2.1			
66	C	7.2.3			
67	B	7.2.4			
68	C	7.3.1			
69	C	7.3.3			
70	B	Alg. 1, 2.0			
71	A	Alg. 1, 3.0			

Answers